GCSE
Success

WORKBOOK

Science

Carla Newman
Joanne Barton
John Sadler
Jon Dwyer
Colin Porter
Charles Cotton

Contents

Contents

Physics (cont.)

Revised

Chemistry

Revised

Contents

A Balanced Diet

Multiple-choice questions

Choose just one answer: A, B, C or D.

1 What are carbohydrates made of? **(1 mark)**
- **A** glycerol
- **B** glucose
- **C** amino acids
- **D** fatty acids

2 Which substance is needed for growth and repair? **(1 mark)**
- **A** carbohydrate
- **B** vitamins
- **C** fats
- **D** protein

3 Kwashiorkor occurs due to a lack of which substance? **(1 mark)**
- **A** protein
- **B** carbohydrate
- **C** vitamin C
- **D** fibre

4 How many main food groups are there? **(1 mark)**
- **A** 5
- **B** 6
- **C** 7
- **D** 8

5 Which of these substances is stored as adipose tissue? **(1 mark)**
- **A** carbohydrates
- **B** minerals
- **C** fats
- **D** protein

Score   / 5

Short-answer questions

1 **True or false?**

	True	False	(4 marks)
a) Proteins can be stored in the body.	☐	☐	
b) First class proteins contain all the essential amino acids.	☐	☐	
c) Plant proteins are examples of first class proteins.	☐	☐	
d) Proteins are made of fatty acids.	☐	☐	

2 List four factors that may affect a person's diet. (4 marks)

i) ....

ii) ....

iii) ....

iv) ....

Score   / 8

Answer all parts of all questions. Continue on a separate sheet of paper if necessary.

1 a) Explain what is meant by the term 'balanced diet'. (1 mark)

....

....

b) In terms of specific nutrients, what might a vegetarian lack in their diet? (1 mark)

....

2 Complete the following sentences. (8 marks)

Fats are composed of .... and ....

They are used by the body as an energy ....

Iron is an example of a .... It is needed to produce ....

Vitamin C prevents the disease called ....

Fibre is composed of ...., which helps prevent ....

3 Estimated average requirement of protein can be calculated using the following formula

EAR (g) = 0.6 × body mass (kg)

a) Calculate the EAR for a woman weighing 60 kg. (1 mark)

b) The woman becomes pregnant. Explain how this will affect her EAR for protein and how she will need to change her diet. (3 marks)

....

....

....

....

Score   / 14

How well did you do?

| 0–6 | Try again | 7–12 | Getting there | 13–19 | Good work | 20–27 | Excellent! |

For more information on this topic, see pages 4–5 of your Success Revision Guide.

Homeostasis

Multiple-choice questions

Choose just one answer: A, B, C or D.

1 Which of the following is a hormone? **(1 mark)**
- **A** glucose
- **B** glucagon
- **C** glycogen
- **D** glycerol

2 Insulin is produced by which organ? **(1 mark)**
- **A** liver
- **B** stomach
- **C** small intestine
- **D** pancreas

3 Cells targeted by insulin respond by converting **(1 mark)**
- **A** glucose to glycogen
- **B** glucose to glucagon
- **C** glycogen to glucose
- **D** glycogen to glycerol

4 People who cannot control their blood sugar level suffer from **(1 mark)**
- **A** diabetes
- **B** anaemia
- **C** malnutrition
- **D** anorexia

5 Homeostasis works by **(1 mark)**
- **A** positive feedback
- **B** neutral feedback
- **C** negative feedback
- **D** limiting feedback

Score / 5

Short-answer questions

1 Complete the following table comparing Type 1 and Type 2 diabetes. (4 marks)

Diabetes	Caused by	Treated by
Type 1		
Type 2		

2 Use the following words to complete the sequence showing control by hormones. (4 marks)

Bloodstream transports hormone   **Target organ**
Gland secretes hormone   **Receptors**

1. Stimulus

2. ....

3. ....

4. ....

5. ....

6. Response

Score / 8

GCSE-style questions

Answer all parts of all questions. Continue on a separate sheet of paper if necessary.

1 Define homeostasis, giving appropriate examples.

(3 marks)

....

....

....

2 The following graph shows the blood sugar level of a diabetes sufferer.

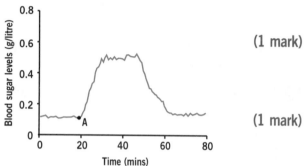

a) What is the normal blood sugar level of this person?

(1 mark)

....

b) What caused the blood sugar level to increase at point A?

(1 mark)

....

c) The person controls their diabetes by injecting insulin. At what time did they give themselves the injection?

(1 mark)

....

d) Which type of diabetes does the person suffer from if they control it by injecting insulin?

(1 mark)

....

e) A healthy person, who does not have diabetes, exercises for an hour. Their blood sugar level decreases below the normal level. Explain how the control mechanism returns the blood sugar level to normal. (You may use flow diagrams.)

(4 marks)

....

....

....

....

3 Temperature control in a house works by negative feedback. Explain what this means and how it works.

(3 marks)

....

....

....

Score   / 14

Biology

How well did you do?

| 0–6 | Try again | 7–12 | Getting there | 13–19 | Good work | 20–27 | Excellent! |

For more information on this topic, see pages 6–7 of your Success Revision Guide.

Hormones and Reproduction

Multiple-choice questions

Choose just one answer: A, B, C or D.

1 Which hormones control the changes during puberty? **(1 mark)**
- **A** oestrogen and progesterone
- **B** oestrogen and testosterone
- **C** progesterone and testosterone
- **D** only testosterone

2 Oestrogen is produced by which organ? **(1 mark)**
- **A** pituitary gland
- **B** testes
- **C** ovaries
- **D** placenta

3 The menstrual cycle occurs over approximately how many days? **(1 mark)**
- **A** 7 days
- **B** 14 days
- **C** 21 days
- **D** 28 days

4 What is the release of the egg from the ovaries called? **(1 mark)**
- **A** ovulation
- **B** menstruation
- **C** fertilisation
- **D** puberty

5 Which hormone maintains the uterus lining? **(1 mark)**
- **A** FSH
- **B** LH
- **C** oestrogen
- **D** progesterone

Score   / 5

Short-answer questions

1 Oral contraceptives prevent the ovaries from producing eggs.

a) Which hormones do they contain? (2 marks)

....

b) Which hormone do they prevent from being produced? (1 mark)

....

c) Where is this hormone produced? (1 mark)

....

2 Fill in the blanks. (5 marks)

The .... sexual characteristics are controlled by hormones. In males this

hormone is .... and in females it is .... After puberty, males

produce .... continuously. Females produce one .... per month.

Score   / 9

Answer all parts of all questions. Continue on a separate sheet of paper if necessary.

1 After puberty, males and females produce sex cells. Complete the table below identifying three other secondary sexual characteristics that occur for each. **(6 marks)**

Male	Female

2 The diagram shows the changes that occur in the uterus during the menstrual cycle.

a) For how many days does menstruation occur? **(1 mark)**

b) Which hormone repairs the uterus lining? **(1 mark)**

Uterus wall rich in blood cells

0   5   14   28   5
Day of Cycle

c) Which hormone triggers ovulation? **(1 mark)**

d) Which two hormones are produced by the ovaries and target the uterus? **(2 marks)**

e) At the end of the cycle the uterus lining did not break down.

   i) Explain why. **(1 mark)**

   ii) Which hormone is therefore still being produced and where is it produced? **(2 marks)**

3 ✎ Explain why a woman may be infertile and how she may be treated. **(6 marks)**

Score   / 20

How well did you do?

| 0–8 | Try again | 9–16 | Getting there | 17–25 | Good work | 26–34 | Excellent! |

For more information on this topic, see pages 8–9 of your Success Revision Guide.

Responding to the Environment

Multiple-choice questions

Choose just one answer: A, B, C or D.

1 A stimulus is detected by which of the following? **(1 mark)**
- **A** receptors
- **B** coordinators
- **C** CNS
- **D** effectors

2 Chemical receptors are found in which sense organ? **(1 mark)**
- **A** eye
- **B** skin
- **C** tongue
- **D** ear

3 The CNS consists of the **(1 mark)**
- **A** spinal cord
- **B** brain
- **C** brain and spinal cord
- **D** brain and neurones

4 What type of vision do predator animals have? **(1 mark)**
- **A** long vision
- **B** short vision
- **C** binocular vision
- **D** monocular vision

5 Accommodation is described as **(1 mark)**
- **A** judging distance
- **B** focusing on near/distant objects
- **C** colour vision
- **D** being long sighted

Score   / 5

Short-answer questions

1 Draw arrows to match the structures to their functions. (7 marks)

cornea	transmits electrical impulse to CNS
pupil	allows light to enter the eye
lens	contains the photoreceptors
retina	main site of refraction
iris	refraction of light for fine focusing
optic nerve	changes the size of the pupil
ciliary muscle	changes the shape of the lens

2 a) What are the light-sensitive cells in the retina called? (2 marks)

b) Which one detects colour? (1 mark)

Score   / 10

Answer all parts of all questions. Continue on a separate sheet of paper if necessary.

1 On this diagram of an eye label structures A to D. (4 marks)

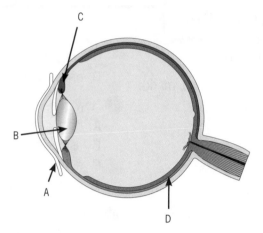

A = ...   B = ...

C = ...   D = ...

2 Complete the following table by crossing out the incorrect option (4 marks)

Object	Ciliary muscle	Suspensory ligament	Lens shape	Light refracted
Distant	**contracted / relaxed**	**tight / slack**	**fatter / thinner**	**a little / a lot**

3 ✏ Explain how organisms respond to changes in the environment. Starting with a stimulus, describe the three main stages that bring about a response. (6 marks)

....

....

....

....

....

....

....

Score   / 14

How well did you do?

| 0–7 | Try again | 8–14 | Getting there | 15–21 | Good work | 22–29 | Excellent! |

For more information on this topic, see pages 10–11 of your Success Revision Guide.

The Nervous System

Multiple-choice questions

Choose just one answer: A, B, C or D.

1 What is a synapse? **(1 mark)**
- **A** a gap between two neurones
- **B** the point where two neurones join
- **C** a chemical
- **D** a neurotransmitter

2 Which neurone carries the electrical impulse to the CNS? **(1 mark)**
- **A** motor
- **B** sensory
- **C** relay
- **D** receptor

3 Complete the following: All reflexes **(1 mark)**
- **A** involve the brain
- **B** are conscious responses

- **C** are very fast
- **D** only involve one neurone

4 How does the neurotransmitter move? **(1 mark)**
- **A** diffusion
- **B** osmosis
- **C** active transport
- **D** electrical impulses

5 Painkillers work by targeting which of the following? **(1 mark)**
- **A** motor neurones
- **B** sensory neurones
- **C** relay neurones
- **D** synapses

Score   / 5

Short-answer questions

1 a) Which type of neurone is shown in the diagram?

.... (1 mark)

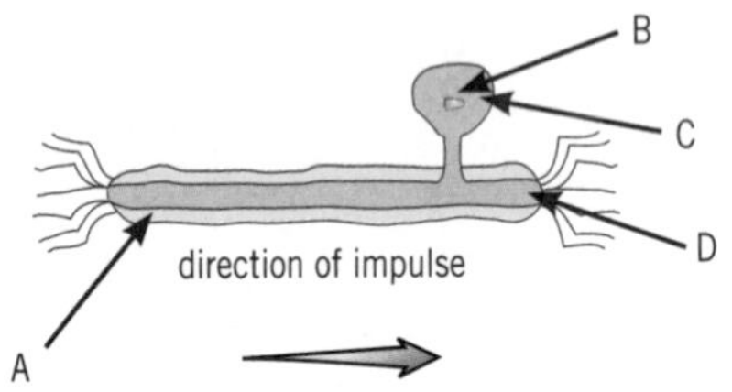

b) Label structures A to D. (4 marks)

direction of impulse

A = ...   B = ...

C = ...   D = ...

2 **True or false?**   True   False   (3 marks)

a) Reflex actions never involve the brain.   ☐   ☐

b) Voluntary actions always involve the brain.   ☐   ☐

c) An electrical impulse can jump the synapse.   ☐   ☐

Score   / 8

Answer all parts of all questions. Continue on a separate sheet of paper if necessary.

1 Neurones are specialised cells. Describe the role of the axon, myelin sheath and dendrites.

(3 marks)

....

....

....

2 These sentences describe how the impulse crosses the synapse, but they are in the wrong order. Fill in the boxes below to show the correct order.

(4 marks)

A Neurotransmitter diffuses across the gap.

B Neurotransmitter joins to receptors.

C Neurotransmitter is released from sensory neurone.

D Electrical impulse formed in relay neurone.

3 The diagram shows the events that occur when a person touches a pin.

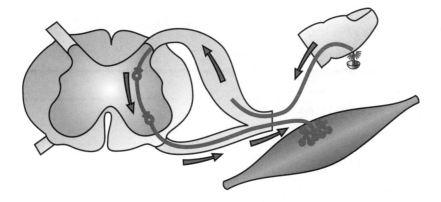

🖉 Describe the reflex action.

(6 marks)

....

....

....

....

....

....

Score   / 13

How well did you do?

| 0–6 | Try again | 7–13 | Getting there | 14–19 | Good work | 20–26 | Excellent! |

For more information on this topic, see pages 12–13 of your Success Revision Guide.

13

Plant Responses

Multiple-choice questions

Choose just one answer: A, B, C or D.

1 Which word describes plant growth, in a particular direction, due to external stimuli? **(1 mark)**
- **A** coordination
- **B** communication
- **C** tropism
- **D** elongation

2 Which of the following describes how roots grow? **(1 mark)**
- **A** away from light and towards water
- **B** away from light
- **C** towards gravity
- **D** away from light and towards gravity

3 Which of the following gardening activities does not involve the use of plant hormones? **(1 mark)**
- **A** killing weeds
- **B** increasing photosynthesis
- **C** producing seedless fruit
- **D** ripening fruit

4 Which of the following does auxin cause? **(1 mark)**
- **A** cell elongation
- **B** cell coordination
- **C** cell division
- **D** cell differentiation

5 Which stimulus negatively controls shoot growth of a seed? **(1 mark)**
- **A** light
- **B** water
- **C** heat
- **D** gravity

Score / 5

Short-answer questions

1 Plants respond to external stimuli.

a) What is the response to light called? (1 mark)

b) What is the response to gravity called? (1 mark)

c) Which hormone brings about these responses? (1 mark)

2 Gardeners make use of plant hormones. Give three uses of plant hormones. (3 marks)

a)

b)

c)

Score / 6

14

Answer all parts of all questions. Continue on a separate sheet of paper if necessary.

1 **a)** Describe the growth of the shoots in the diagram.

(1 mark)

....

....

b) Explain what is happening within the shoots to make this occur.

(3 marks)

....

....

....

2 🖊 The diagrams illustrate the response of a shoot and a root when a plant is placed on its side. Using the diagrams, explain what will happen to both the roots and stems.

(6 marks)

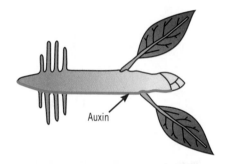

....

....

....

....

....

....

....

....

....

3 Seeds germinate underground. Explain why the shoot still grows towards the light. (1 mark)

....

Score   / 11

Biology

How well did you do?

| 0–5 | Try again | 6–11 | Getting there | 12–17 | Good work | 18–22 | Excellent! |

For more information on this topic, see pages 14–15 of your Success Revision Guide.

Pathogens and Infections

Multiple-choice questions

Choose just one answer: A, B, C or D.

1 Which is an example of an infectious disease? **(1 mark)**
- **A** diabetes
- **B** scurvy
- **C** malaria
- **D** cancer

2 Which of the following is caused by fungi? **(1 mark)**
- **A** athlete's foot
- **B** flu
- **C** cholera
- **D** anaemia

3 How is HIV spread? **(1 mark)**
- **A** contact
- **B** air
- **C** body fluids
- **D** vectors

4 Which word completes the following? Tears contain lysozyme, which acts as an **(1 mark)**
- **A** antigen
- **B** antibody
- **C** antiseptic
- **D** antibiotic

5 Which of the following is not a natural defence against disease? **(1 mark)**
- **A** stomach acid
- **B** skin
- **C** sweating
- **D** mucus

Score / 5

Short-answer questions

1 Complete the following passage using the most appropriate word(s). (9 marks)

Pathogens, for example .... and ...., lead to

.... diseases. Flu is caused by a ...., which is transmitted in

the .... Pathogens have chemicals on their surface called

.... These are detected by .... cells and produce

.... which have a .... shape.

2 The skin acts as a barrier, preventing pathogens from entering the body. Describe three other protective mechanisms. (3 marks)

Score / 12

GCSE-style questions

Answer all parts of all questions. Continue on a separate sheet of paper if necessary.

1 Malaria is an infectious disease.

    a) Which type of organism is it caused by? .... (1 mark)

    b) How is it transmitted? (2 marks)

    c) How can its spread be controlled? (3 marks)

2 Distinguish between the following.

    a) antigens and antibodies (2 marks)

    b) lymphocyte and phagocyte (2 marks)

3 True or false?

	True	False	(4 marks)
a) Flu is transmitted by body fluids.	☐	☐	
b) Red-green colour blindness is a deficiency disease.	☐	☐	
c) Stomach acid is useful in preventing salmonella entering the body.	☐	☐	
d) Memory cells are produced by the brain.	☐	☐	

4 a) Explain how phagocytes kill bacteria. (2 marks)

    b) A person has had chicken pox. Explain why this person will not suffer from chicken pox again. (4 marks)

Score   / 20

How well did you do?

| 0–9 | Try again | 10–18 | Getting there | 19–27 | Good work | 28–37 | Excellent! |

For more information on this topic, see pages 16–17 of your Success Revision Guide.

Antibiotics and Antiseptics

Multiple-choice questions

Choose just one answer: A, B, C or D.

1 Which of the following diseases is treated by antibiotics? **(1 mark)**
- **A** HIV
- **B** cholera
- **C** flu
- **D** malaria

2 If the skin is cut, which method would be used to prevent a skin infection? **(1 mark)**
- **A** antibiotics
- **B** disinfectants
- **C** antiseptics
- **D** soap

3 What are antibiotics produced by? **(1 mark)**
- **A** bacteria
- **B** fungi
- **C** viruses
- **D** plants

4 Which of the following is an aseptic technique? **(1 mark)**
- **A** sterilising the inoculating loop
- **B** using antibiotics
- **C** washing hands with water
- **D** using agar

5 Which is an antibiotic-resistant bacteria? **(1 mark)**
- **A** MMR
- **B** MRSA
- **C** HIV
- **D** AIDS

Score   / 5

Short-answer questions

1 a) In laboratories, what is the name of the jelly on which microorganisms are grown? (1 mark)

b) What does this jelly contain? (2 marks)

c) State two precautions used to prevent contamination of the jelly. (2 marks)

2 Use these words to fill in the gaps. (4 marks)

antiseptic   disinfectant   antibiotics

.... are produced by fungi.

.... and .... kill 99.9% of bacteria.

.... works on the skin's surface.

Score   / 9

Biology

18

Answer all parts of all questions. Continue on a separate sheet of paper if necessary.

1 An investigation into the effectiveness of antibiotics was carried out. Discs containing antibiotic A to H were placed on agar that had bacteria growing on it. The diagram below shows the results.

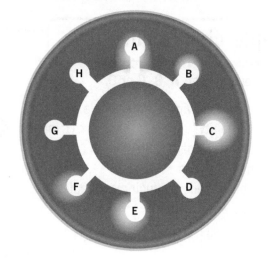

a) Why are the bacteria grown on agar? (1 mark)

....

....

b) Explain why some discs did not kill the bacteria. (1 mark)

....

c) Which was the best antibiotic for this bacteria? Explain your reason. (2 marks)

....

....

d) Name a common antibiotic. (1 mark)

....

2 Antibiotic-resistant bacteria are becoming an increasing problem for doctors.

a) What phenomena leads to antibiotic-resistant bacteria? (1 mark)

....

b) What precautions should we take to prevent more bacteria becoming resistant? (2 marks)

....

....

c) How are hospitals trying to prevent the spread of antibiotic resistance? (3 marks)

....

....

....

....

Score   / 11

Biology

How well did you do?

| 0–6 | Try again | 7–12 | Getting there | 13–19 | Good work | 20–25 | Excellent! |

For more information on this topic, see pages 18–19 of your Success Revision Guide.

19

Vaccinations

Multiple-choice questions

Choose just one answer: A, B, C or D.

1 Which of the following is an example of passive immunity? **(1 mark)**
  A injecting dead pathogens
  B injecting antigens
  C white blood cells producing antibodies
  D injecting antibodies

2 Which of the following do vaccines NOT contain? **(1 mark)**
  A antigens
  B dead pathogens
  C living pathogens
  D weakened pathogens

3 Long-term immunity occurs due to which of the following? **(1 mark)**
  A antibodies
  B memory cells
  C brain cells
  D red blood cells

4 A vaccine for the bacteria salmonella gives immunity against **(1 mark)**
  A salmonella
  B salmonella and flu
  C chicken pox and salmonella
  D all bacterial pathogens

5 Which of the following can cause deafness? **(1 mark)**
  A measles
  B mumps
  C rubella
  D rickets

Score   / 5

Short-answer questions

1 True or false?   True   False   (5 marks)

  a) Vaccinations carry no risks of developing the infectious disease.   ☐   ☐

  b) Active immunity produces memory cells.   ☐   ☐

  c) Flu vaccine is given yearly.   ☐   ☐

  d) MMR vaccine is given yearly.   ☐   ☐

  e) Breast milk contains antibodies.   ☐   ☐

2 Why are vaccines specific?   (2 marks)

Score   / 7

Answer all parts of all questions. Continue on a separate sheet of paper if necessary.

1 **a)** Why may someone be injected with an antibody? (1 mark)

....

b) How does this immunity differ from when the antibodies are produced by the person's white blood cells? (2 marks)

....

....

2 ✎ Distinguish between active and passive immunity, giving examples of each. (6 marks)

....

....

....

....

....

3 **a)** Which diseases does MMR protect against? (3 marks)

....

b) What is the risk to a pregnant woman if she has not had her MMR? (1 mark)

....

c) Suggest two concerns regarding giving the MMR vaccination. (2 marks)

....

....

....

4 Explain why the flu vaccine is only effective for one year (2 marks)

....

....

Score   / 17

Biology

How well did you do?

| 0–7 | Try again | 8–14 | Getting there | 15–21 | Good work | 22–29 | Excellent! |

For more information on this topic, see pages 20–21 of your Success Revision Guide.

Drugs

Multiple-choice questions

Choose just one answer: A, B, C or D.

1 Alcohol is a   **(1 mark)**
- **A** depressant
- **B** stimulant
- **C** placebo
- **D** painkiller

2 Which class of drugs is the most dangerous?   **(1 mark)**
- **A** A
- **B** B
- **C** C
- **D** X

3 Which of the following is a class A drug?   **(1 mark)**
- **A** nicotine
- **B** antibiotics
- **C** cannabis
- **D** heroin

4 Which type of drug blocks the transmission of nerve impulses?   **(1 mark)**
- **A** depressants
- **B** stimulants
- **C** placebos
- **D** class A

5 Which of the following best describes cannabis?   **(1 mark)**
- **A** class A
- **B** available on prescription
- **C** illegal
- **D** not addictive

Score   / 5

Short-answer questions

1 Define the following terms.

  a) Addictive .... **(1 mark)**

  b) Tolerance .... **(1 mark)**

2 a) Thalidomide was used to treat morning sickness in pregnant woman. Why was the drug later banned from use in pregnancy?   **(1 mark)**

  _____

  b) What is thalidomide now used to treat? .... **(1 mark)**

3 True or false?

	True	False	(3 marks)
a) Cocaine is a class C drug.	☐	☐	
b) Drugs alter the functioning of the body.	☐	☐	
c) Double blind testing of drugs is when only the doctor knows which the placebo is.	☐	☐	

Score   / 7

GCSE-style questions

Answer all parts of all questions. Continue on a separate sheet of paper if necessary.

1 A new drug is being developed to treat a skin condition.

   a) Why does the drug need to be tested before it can be used on patients? **(2 marks)**

   ....

   ....

   b) How will the drug be tested? **(2 marks)**

   ....

   ....

   c) What are the ethical issues of testing on animals? **(2 marks)**

   ....

   ....

2 Drug A was trialled on ten patients. The patients were split into two groups. One group was given drug A; the other group was given a placebo. It was a blind test.

   a) What is a placebo and why is it given? **(2 marks)**

   ....

   ....

   b) What does 'it was a blind test' mean? **(1 mark)**

   ....

   c) What is the advantage of carrying out a 'blind test'? **(1 mark)**

   ....

   d) How could this trial be made more reliable? **(1 mark)**

   ....

3 Compare the effects of a stimulant and a depressant on the nervous system. **(2 marks)**

....

....

....

Score   / 13

How well did you do?

| 0–6 | Try again | 7–12 | Getting there | 13–19 | Good work | 20–25 | Excellent! |

For more information on this topic, see pages 22–23 of your Success Revision Guide.

Genes and Chromosomes

Multiple-choice questions

Choose just one answer: A, B, C or D.

1 Which sex chromosomes do females have? **(1 mark)**
- **A** XX
- **B** XY
- **C** YY
- **D** X

2 Gametes have how many chromosomes? **(1 mark)**
- **A** 12
- **B** 23
- **C** 46
- **D** 92

3 Where is the genetic material found? **(1 mark)**
- **A** nucleus
- **B** cytoplasm
- **C** mitochondria
- **D** chloroplasts

4 What is the joining of two gametes called? **(1 mark)**
- **A** mutations
- **B** DNA
- **C** variation
- **D** fertilisation

5 A random change in a gene is due to what? **(1 mark)**
- **A** variation
- **B** mutation
- **C** sexual reproduction
- **D** asexual reproduction

Score   / 5

Short-answer questions

1 Match the words to the correct definitions. (3 marks)

gene	structure found in the nucleus
DNA	codes for a protein
chromosome	chemical containing four different bases

2 a) What does DNA stand for? (1 mark)

....

b) What are the four chemical bases found in DNA? (4 marks)

....

3 Complete the blanks. (3 marks)

Human body cells have .... chromosomes. Sex cells are called

.... Following fertilisation the cell formed is called a ....

Score   / 11

Biology

Answer all parts of all questions. Continue on a separate sheet of paper if necessary.

1 **a)** Complete the diagram showing how sex is determined. (3 marks)

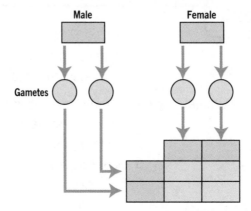

b) A couple have two daughters. What is the probability that their next child will be a daughter? (1 mark)

....

2 Explain why sexual reproduction results in variation. (2 marks)

....

....

3 Differences are due to variation. Complete the table below by

a) stating the two causes of variation (2 marks)

b) giving two examples of each. (4 marks)

Cause of variation	Examples
	1.
	2.
	1.
	2.

Score / 12

How well did you do?

| 0–7 | Try again | 8–14 | Getting there | 15–21 | Good work | 22–28 | Excellent! |

For more information on this topic, see pages 24–25 of your Success Revision Guide.

Biology

Passing on Genes

Multiple-choice questions

Choose just one answer: A, B, C or D.

1 Which of the following is not a genetic disorder? **(1 mark)**
- **A** anaemia
- **B** cystic fibrosis
- **C** Huntington's
- **D** sickle-cell anaemia

2 Alternative copies of a gene are called? **(1 mark)**
- **A** DNA
- **B** alleles
- **C** dominant
- **D** recessive

3 Which disease causes thick mucus and breathing problems? **(1 mark)**
- **A** anaemia
- **B** cystic fibrosis
- **C** Huntington's
- **D** sickle-cell anaemia

4 Which word describes a person with two copies of the same allele? **(1 mark)**
- **A** homozygous
- **B** heterozygous
- **C** recessive
- **D** dominant

5 Which allele is always expressed in the phenotype? **(1 mark)**
- **A** homozygous
- **B** heterozygous
- **C** recessive
- **D** dominant

Score / 5

Short-answer questions

1 Match the terms to the correct definitions. (4 marks)

recessive	The two alleles inherited for a gene are the same
homozygous	Alleles an organism carries
genotype	Characteristics expressed
phenotype	Allele only shown in characteristic if two are inherited

2 Huntington's chorea is caused by a dominant allele. Complete the genetic cross for a normal parent and a heterozygous sufferer. (4 marks)

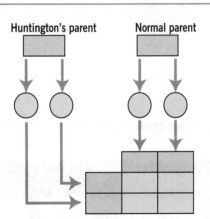

Huntington's parent   Normal parent

Score / 8

Answer all parts of all questions. Continue on a separate sheet of paper if necessary.

1 Genetic screening can be carried out on a foetus.

    a) Give an advantage and a disadvantage of genetic screening for the parents.   **(2 marks)**

    ....

    ....

    b) What are the ethical considerations? ....   **(2 marks)**

    ....

2 Cystic fibrosis is a genetic disease caused by a recessive allele. A couple
who are both carriers of the recessive allele for cystic fibrosis are expecting
a child. What is the probability their child will suffer from cystic fibrosis?
Draw a genetic diagram on a separate sheet of paper.   **(5 marks)**

Probability = ...

3 Sickle cell anaemia is a genetic disease that affects the red blood cells.

    a) Is it caused by a dominant or a recessive allele? ....   **(1 mark)**

    b) What are the symptoms of the disease? ....   **(2 marks)**

    ....

4 The diagram shows a family tree for the
inheritance of cystic fibrosis.

    a) What evidence is there that cystic fibrosis
is coded for by a recessive allele?   **(2 marks)**

    ....

    ....

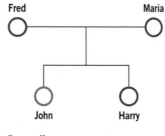

    b) Are cystic fibrosis sufferers heterozygous or homozygous? ....   **(1 mark)**

    c) What are the symptoms of cystic fibrosis? ....   **(2 marks)**

    ....

Score   / 17

Biology

How well did you do?

| 0–7 | Try again | 8–15 | Getting there | 16–23 | Good work | 24–30 | Excellent! |

For more information on this topic, see pages 26–27 of your Success Revision Guide.

Gene Technology

Multiple-choice questions

Choose just one answer: A, B, C or D.

1 Genetic diseases can be treated using which of the following? **(1 mark)**
- **A** stem cells
- **B** clones
- **C** tissue culture
- **D** body cells

2 What is a clone? **(1 mark)**
- **A** similar organisms
- **B** different organisms
- **C** genetically identical organisms
- **D** genetically engineered organisms

3 Dolly the sheep was produced by which method? **(1 mark)**
- **A** cloning adult cells
- **B** cloning embryos

- **C** gene therapy
- **D** genetic engineering

4 Which of the following can be treated by gene therapy? **(1 mark)**
- **A** obesity
- **B** heart disease
- **C** scurvy
- **D** cystic fibrosis

5 What is the term for growing a new plant from a small group of cells? **(1 mark)**
- **A** genetic modification
- **B** cuttings
- **C** gene therapy
- **D** tissue culture

Score / 5

Short-answer questions

1 The diagram shows how Dolly the sheep was cloned.

a) From what type of cell was the DNA extracted to clone Dolly?

....

b) Why was the nucleus removed from sheep B's cell?

....

....

c) The lamb is a clone to which sheep? Give a reason for your answer.

....

....

A   B

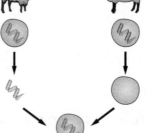

Cell taken from Sheep A

DNA extracted

Egg cell taken from Sheep B

Nucleus removed **(1 mark)**

(1 mark)

Fused cell develops into embryo...

DNA from Sheep A fused with egg cell from Sheep B

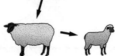

... which is placed in uterus of surrogate mother

Lamb

(2 marks)

Score / 4

GCSE-style questions

Answer all parts of all questions. Continue on a separate sheet of paper if necessary.

1 Describe how plants can be cloned from cuttings and from small groups of cells.　(3 marks)

....

....

....

2 The following sentences describe the process of genetic engineering, but they are in
the wrong order. Put them in the correct order in the boxes provided.　(5 marks)

A The gene is cut using an enzyme.

B The plasmid is cut using an enzyme and the gene is inserted.

C The gene is identified from the strand of DNA.

D The bacteria multiply to form clones.

E The plasmid is put back in the bacterium.

3 a) What are stem cells?　(1 mark)

....

b) How could stem cells be used by doctors?　(1 mark)

....

4 Why are identical twins clones?　(2 marks)

....

....

5 a) Give two examples of why crops may be genetically modified.　(2 marks)

....

....

b) GM crops are very controversial. Give two arguments for GM crops and two against
GM crops. (Answer on a separate sheet of paper.)　(4 marks)

Score　/ 18

How well did you do?

| 0–6 Try again | 7–12 Getting there | 13–19 Good work | 20–27 Excellent! |

For more information on this topic, see pages 28–29 of your Success Revision Guide.

29

Evolution and Natural Selection

Multiple-choice questions

Choose just one answer: A, B, C or D.

1 What evidence is there for evolution? **(1 mark)**
- **A** photos
- **B** documents
- **C** fossils
- **D** plants

2 Whose theory of evolution is generally believed? **(1 mark)**
- **A** Darwin
- **B** Lamarck
- **C** Mendel
- **D** Newton

3 Natural selection can be considered as which of the following? **(1 mark)**
- **A** survival of the fittest
- **B** variation
- **C** selective breeding
- **D** artificial selection

4 Which of the following is an example of natural selection? **(1 mark)**
- **A** GM crops
- **B** Dolly the sheep
- **C** antibiotic-resistant bacteria
- **D** genetically modifying bacteria to produce insulin

5 Following the industrial revolution, why were more dark peppered moths found? **(1 mark)**
- **A** flew away from predators faster
- **B** protected species
- **C** better camouflaged from predators
- **D** poisonous to predators

Score   / 5

Short-answer questions

1 What is evolution? (2 marks)

....

....

2 Complete the following. (5 marks)

Darwin called his theory .... It was based on these four observations:

a) Organisms produce .... numbers of offspring.

b) Population numbers .... over long time periods.

c) Organisms of the same species are all slightly different: they show ....

d) These beneficial characteristics can be .... from their parents.

Score   / 7

Answer all parts of all questions. Continue on a separate sheet of paper if necessary.

1 Lamarck's theory states that giraffes' long necks developed due to
them stretching for food. What evidence is there against his theory? **(2 marks)**

....

....

2 Why do some organisms become extinct? **(2 marks)**

....

....

....

3 Peppered moths evolved so that in industrial areas a dark variety was
more prominent.

a) Why are there more dark peppered moths in industrial areas? **(2 marks)**

....

....

b) What caused the change in the peppered moths' colour? **(1 mark)**

....

c) Use Darwin's theory to explain why the population of dark peppered
moths increased. **(4 marks)**

....

....

....

....

Score   / 11

How well did you do?

| 0–5 | Try again | 6–11 | Getting there | 12–17 | Good work | 18–23 | Excellent! |

For more information on this topic, see pages 30–31 of your Success Revision Guide.

Competition and Adaptation

Multiple-choice questions

Choose just one answer: A, B, C or D.

1 Animals which are adapted to live in a specific area are known as... **(1 mark)**
   A specialists
   B opportunists
   C generalists
   D analysts

2 Which word describes the place where an organism lives along with its role there? **(1 mark)**
   A resource
   B habitat
   C competition
   D niche

3 Which of these do plants NOT compete for? **(1 mark)**
   A light
   B food

   C minerals
   D water

4 Desert, arctic, tundra, savannah and pond are all examples of... **(1 mark)**
   A climates
   B habitats
   C niches
   D organisms

5 Which of these is NOT a behavioural adaptation? **(1 mark)**
   A being nocturnal
   B migration
   C having wings
   D hibernation

Score   / 5

Short-answer questions

1 Fill in the gaps in the following paragraph using these words. (6 marks)

intraspecific   interspecific   adaptations   habitat   population   compete

When resources in a .... are limited, organisms will ....

for them. This competition can be from organisms of the same species

(................................ competition) or from organisms in other species

(................................ competition). The organisms that have better ....

to their environments will be more likely to survive to produce offspring. This means

successful adaptations are likely to survive in the ....

2 Circle any adaptations likely to be present in prey species. (2 marks)

**camouflage   binocular vision   monocular vision
pointed canine teeth   thorns**

Score   / 8

Answer all parts of all questions. Continue on a separate sheet of paper if necessary.

1 Draw a line linking the organism to its adaptation and then another line to link it to the reason for this adaptation.

(5 marks)

Organism	Adaptation	Reason
owl	binocular vision	silent flight
wolf	sharp teeth	to give better vision of predators
rabbit	layer of thick blubber beneath the skin	for ripping meat
seal	velvety down feathers	camouflage against the reef
clownfish	striped colouring	to keep warm

2 Explain why animals which lay eggs are more likely to produce offspring in greater numbers than animals which give birth to live young.

(2 marks)

3 ✏ Explain why an elephant must eat about 7% of its body weight daily whereas a mouse needs to consume about 25% of its own body weight in the same period. You should consider in your answer: surface area to volume ratio, level of activity and habitat.

(6 marks)

Score   / 13

Biology

How well did you do?

| 0–6 | Try again | 7–13 | Getting there | 14–19 | Good work | 20–26 | Excellent! |

For more information on this topic, see pages 32–33 of your Success Revision Guide.

Energy Flow

Multiple-choice questions

Choose just one answer: A, B, C or D.

1 Which of these is a producer? **(1 mark)**
- **A** ladybird
- **B** mouse
- **C** giraffe
- **D** oak tree

2 Which of these is NOT a way that energy is lost from food chains? **(1 mark)**
- **A** biomass
- **B** excretion
- **C** egestion
- **D** respiration

3 Which of these is produced by egestion? **(1 mark)**
- **A** urine
- **B** faeces
- **C** sweat
- **D** exhaled air

4 What process, other than photosynthesis, might qualify an organism as a producer? **(1 mark)**
- **A** respiration
- **B** homeostasis
- **C** chemosynthesis
- **D** osmosis

5 Which of these are the raw material requirements for photosynthesis to take place? **(1 mark)**
- **A** light and glucose
- **B** glucose and oxygen
- **C** carbon dioxide and water
- **D** carbon dioxide and oxygen

Score / 5

Short-answer questions

1 What feature of birds and mammals means that they lose more energy from a food chain than would be lost by the equivalent mass of reptiles, fish or amphibians? (1 mark)

....

2 Fill in the gaps using these words. You may use the words more than once. (9 marks)

energy   water   more   dry   dead   biomass   trophic

In a pyramid of ...., we represent the amount of .... at each

.... level with a bar whose size is proportional to the amount of ....

at that level. Fresh biomass includes the .... contained by an organism, but since

water contains no useable ...., this can be deceptive. .... biomass

is a better reflection of the amount of energy there is at each level of a food chain, but to dry

organisms out, they must be .... This conflicts with scientists' ideas about

conservation. Another difficulty in estimating biomass occurs when animals feed at

.... than one trophic level.

Score / 10

Answer all parts of all questions. Continue on a separate sheet of paper if necessary.

1 Some farmers choose to restrict the movement of their animals to maximise meat production. Explain how this works. **(2 marks)**

....

....

2 Read the information below. Use this and your knowledge of food chains and pyramids of biomass to answer the questions that follow.

In the 1960s, a pesticide called DDT was widely used to increase crop yield. It worked by poisoning the insects that ate the crops. Once inside the body of an animal, DDT takes a very long time to break down.

Pesticide which fell onto the soil was washed into water courses in rainwater. Environmentalists saw a correlation in the use of DDT and the decline in the number of grebes and fish in affected areas. They lobbied for a change in the law and DDT was withdrawn from use.

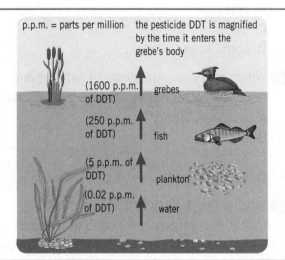

p.p.m. = parts per million   the pesticide DDT is magnified by the time it enters the grebe's body

(1600 p.p.m. of DDT) — grebes

(250 p.p.m. of DDT) — fish

(5 p.p.m. of DDT) — plankton

(0.02 p.p.m. of DDT) — water

a) Explain why the poison killed more grebes than it did fish. **(4 marks)**

....

....

b) What is meant by the term 'correlation'? **(1 mark)**

....

c) What evidence could the environmentalists have provided to support their view? **(3 marks)**

....

....

....

3 In a food web, foxes prey on rabbits, mistle thrushes and dormice. Barn owls prey on dormice. Explain why the number of barn owls is more likely to be affected than the number of foxes, if the number of dormice falls. **(2 marks)**

....

....

Score   / 12

Biology

How well did you do?

| 0–6 | Try again | 7–12 | Getting there | 13–19 | Good work | 20–27 | Excellent! |

For more information on this topic, see pages 34–35 of your Success Revision Guide.

Recycling

Multiple-choice questions

Choose just one answer: A, B, C or D.

1 Which of these is a decomposer? **(1 mark)**
  A fungi
  B grass
  C oak
  D corn

2 Which of these conditions will help prevent decay by (most) bacteria? **(1 mark)**
  A well oxygenated
  B acidic
  C damp
  D warm

3 What name is given to decaying plant matter that gardeners may add to fertilise their soil? **(1 mark)**
  A compost
  B mess

  C decomposers
  D fungi

4 Decomposers are useful to plants because they recycle what back into the soil? **(1 mark)**
  A water
  B light
  C minerals
  D carbon dioxide

5 Which chemical do nitrifying bacteria convert to nitrogen? **(1 mark)**
  A ammonia
  B nitrogen
  C oxygen
  D carbon dioxide

Score / 5

Short-answer questions

1 Name three processes that release CO_2 into the air. .... (3 marks)

....

2 The arrows in the picture show carbon transfer in the carbon cycle. Match the letters A–F with the processes.

(6 marks)

	death
	feeding
	combustion
	decomposition
	respiration
	photosynthesis

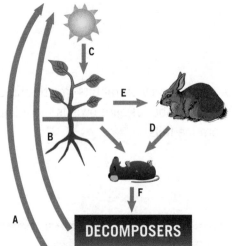

Score / 9

GCSE-style questions

Answer all parts of all questions. Continue on a separate sheet of paper if necessary.

1 These questions are about the nitrogen cycle.

   a) What organisms are responsible for converting nitrogen in the soil into nitrates

   that are useable by the plant? .... **(1 mark)**

   b) Why is nitrogen unusable whereas nitrates are useable? **(2 marks)**

   ....

   c) What role does lightning play in the nitrogen cycle? **(1 mark)**

   ....

2 The graph shows what happens to the
   rate at which bacteria work at different
   temperatures.

   a) Describe the relationship between
   temperature and rate of decay.

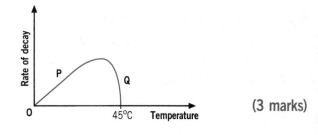

   (3 marks)

   ....

   ....

   ....

   b) Explain the relationship you have described. **(2 marks)**

   ....

   ....

   c) Related to this correlation, explain why it is necessary to turn a compost heap over
   in order to keep the decay continuous. **(3 marks)**

   ....

   ....

   ....

3 What would happen if there were no decomposers in an ecosystem? **(1 mark)**

   ....

   ....

Score   / 13

How well did you do?

| 0–6 | Try again | 7–12 | Getting there | 13–19 | Good work | 20–27 | Excellent! |

For more information on this topic, see pages 36–37 of your Success Revision Guide.

Biology

Populations and Pollution

Multiple-choice questions

Choose just one answer: A, B, C or D.

1 Which of these pollutants does not contribute to global warming? **(1 mark)**
- **A** carbon dioxide
- **B** sulfur dioxide
- **C** heavy metals
- **D** methane

2 Which of these species might be used as an indicator for identifying polluted water? **(1 mark)**
- **A** black spot fungus
- **B** lichen
- **C** mayfly nymph
- **D** rose

3 What is the best term to indicate an ever increasing population size? **(1 mark)**
- **A** exponential growth
- **B** increased birth rate
- **C** increased death rate
- **D** stationary phase

4 Plants use nitrogen to make **(1 mark)**
- **A** carbohydrates
- **B** fats
- **C** proteins
- **D** vitamins

5 Which of these countries is likely to have the largest carbon footprint? **(1 mark)**
- **A** England
- **B** Spain
- **C** China
- **D** India

Score   / 5

Short-answer questions

1 Match the pollutants with the problems they cause. (4 marks)

Pollutants	Problems they cause
carbon dioxide	polluted rivers and lakes
fertilisers & sewage	the greenhouse effect
heavy metals	landfill sites releasing gases
domestic waste	accumulates in food chains

2 a) The risk of developing which medical condition has increased as a result of the destruction of the ozone layer? .... (1 mark)

b) Name one gas thought to be responsible for making holes in the ozone layer. (1 mark)

....

c) Name one source of this gas. .... (1 mark)

Score   / 7

GCSE-style questions

Answer all parts of all questions. Continue on a separate sheet of paper if necessary.

1 ✎ Describe how the greenhouse effect leads to global warming. (Answer on a separate sheet of paper.) **(6 marks)**

2 List the possible consequences of global warming. (Answer on a separate sheet of paper.) **(6 marks)**

3 Study the graph.

a) Describe the general correlation between the number of people with skin cancer and the amount of ozone.

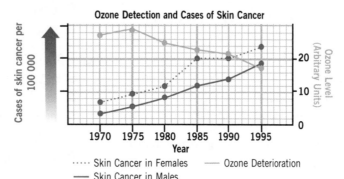

Ozone Detection and Cases of Skin Cancer

····· Skin Cancer in Females   —— Ozone Deterioration
—— Skin Cancer in Males

(2 marks)

....

....

b) Make a suggestion as to the mechanism that might explain this correlation. **(2 marks)**

....

c) Does all the information on the graph agree with this trend? Justify your answer. **(2 marks)**

....

....

4 a) What environmental problem is posed by increased sulfur dioxide production? **(1 mark)**

....

b) What property of this gas makes it particularly dangerous in this way? **(1 mark)**

....

5 Describe the stages of eutrophication that lead to decreased biodiversity in lakes. (Answer on a separate sheet of paper.) **(6 marks)**

Score   / 26

How well did you do?

| 0–10 | Try again | 11–20 | Getting there | 21–30 | Good work | 31–38 | Excellent! |

For more information on this topic, see pages 38–39 of your Success Revision Guide.

Biology

The Electricity Supply

Multiple-choice questions

Choose just one answer: A, B, C or D.

1 Which of the following is a primary energy resource? **(1 mark)**
- **A** mains electricity
- **B** uranium fuel in a nuclear power station
- **C** heat from a radiator
- **D** the kinetic energy of a turbine

2 What type of diagram can be used to illustrate energy transfers? **(1 mark)**
- **A** Gantt chart
- **B** ray diagram
- **C** Sankey diagram
- **D** Venn diagram

3 Which of the following can be used to generate electricity without the need for movement? **(1 mark)**
- **A** tidal energy
- **B** geothermal energy
- **C** chemical energy in natural gas
- **D** solar energy

4 Which of the following is a secondary energy resource? **(1 mark)**
- **A** electrical energy from a battery
- **B** nuclear energy
- **C** coal
- **D** wave energy

5 In a petrol-driven engine there are many energy transfers taking place. Which type of energy is considered to be wasted energy? **(1 mark)**
- **A** electrical
- **B** nuclear
- **C** heat
- **D** kinetic

Score   / 5

Short-answer questions

1 a) Draw a Sankey diagram to show the energy transfers that take place in a light bulb with an input energy of 100 J and an efficiency of 10%. **(3 marks)**

b) For the diagram above, state the type of energy for each of the following: **(3 marks)**

  i) input ....

  ii) useful output ....

  iii) wasted ....

2 For every 1 kg of coal burned in a power station, 8.4 MJ of electrical energy and 15.6 MJ of heat energy are produced. Calculate the % efficiency of electricity generation. **(2 marks)**

Score   / 8

Answer all parts of all questions. Continue on a separate sheet of paper if necessary.

1 With traditional fuels, such as coal, being in finite supply there is much interest in developing renewable energy resources. One possible source is solar energy.

a) There are two ways of using solar energy - by installing 'passive' or 'active' solar panels.

Describe the difference between the 'passive' and 'active' harnessing of solar energy. **(2 marks)**

....

....

b) State one advantage and one disadvantage of using solar energy in the UK. **(2 marks)**

....

....

c) Commercial solar panels are made from lots of 'cells'. On average, each cell has an efficiency of 15%. State what is meant by the term 'efficiency'? **(1 mark)**

....

d) Globally, the average electrical output of a coal-burning power station is 310 J for every 1 kJ of energy input as fuel.

Calculate the average efficiency of a coal-burning power station. **(1 mark)**

....

e) i) 'Energy is always conserved.' Describe what this statement means. **(1 mark)**

....

ii) If energy is always conserved, describe why the energy output by power-stations and solar cells as electricity does not match the total energy input. **(2 marks)**

....

....

f) The EU has set a target of increasing the use of renewable energy to 20% by 2020. Suggest two issues that need to be addressed to help achieve this target. **(2 marks)**

....

....

....

Score /11

Physics

How well did you do?

| 0–6 | Try again | 7–12 | Getting there | 13–18 | Good work | 19–24 | Excellent! |

For more information on this topic, see pages 42–43 of your Success Revision Guide.

Generating Electricity

Multiple-choice questions

Choose just one answer: A, B, C or D.

1 Which of the following energy resources is a fossil fuel? **(1 mark)**
- **A** oil
- **B** nuclear
- **C** wind
- **D** geothermal

2 Which of the following sequences correctly describes the energy transfers taking place in a coal-fired power station? **(1 mark)**
- **A** heat – chemical – kinetic – electrical
- **B** chemical – kinetic – heat – electrical
- **C** heat – chemical – kinetic – electrical
- **D** chemical – heat – kinetic – electrical

3 Which of these devices produces electricity? **(1 mark)**
- **A** bulb
- **B** transformer
- **C** dynamo
- **D** resistor

4 Which of the following non-renewable energy resources does not emit carbon dioxide gas into our atmosphere during energy transfer? **(1 mark)**
- **A** oil
- **B** nuclear
- **C** coal
- **D** natural gas

5 Which of the following is not needed for electromagnetic induction to take place? **(1 mark)**
- **A** coil
- **B** movement
- **C** magnet
- **D** heat

Score / 5

Short-answer questions

1 a) This diagram represents a coal-burning power station. Add labels to complete the diagram. (4 marks)

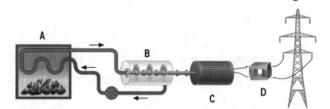

b) Describe the functions of the following devices on the diagram above: (3 marks)

i) Device B ....

ii) Device C ....

c) Describe why coal, oil and gas are called fossil fuels. (1 mark)

....

....

Score / 8

Answer all parts of all questions. Continue on a separate sheet of paper if necessary.

1 The Government is considering opening a new power station in the highlands of Scotland.

a) One of the main objectives is to ensure that the power station does not emit carbon dioxide. A local councillor suggests using biofuels.

   i) Describe why biofuels are **not** a suitable option. (1 mark)

   ....

   ii) Suggest why the councillor might have thought that biofuels would be suitable. Explain your answer. (3 marks)

   ....

   ....

   ....

   iii) State two types of biofuels. (2 marks)

   ....

b) List three important factors that must be considered when choosing a suitable site for a new power station. (3 marks)

   ....

   ....

   ....

c) Ring the correct options to complete this explanation of the role of generators in the new power station.

The generator will induce a **voltage / current / dynamo** using coils of wire and an electromagnet. The electromagnet **remains stationary / rotates / moves up and down** inside the coils of wire so that the coils are in a **positive / negative / changing** magnetic field. (3 marks)

d) The Government decides that nuclear fuel is the most suitable fuel for the power station. They know that this will raise some concerns from the local population and want to prepare for this before announcing their proposal. Suggest two specific factors they should research before making their announcement. (2 marks)

   ....

   ....

Score / 14

Physics

How well did you do?

| 0–8 | Try again | 9–14 | Getting there | 15–20 | Good work | 21–27 | Excellent! |

For more information on this topic, see pages 44–45 of your Success Revision Guide.

Renewable Sources of Energy

Multiple-choice questions

Choose just one answer: A, B, C or D.

1 Which of the following is NOT a renewable energy resource? **(1 mark)**
- **A** geothermal energy
- **B** nuclear fuel
- **C** biofuel
- **D** solar energy

2 Which of these renewable energy resources emits carbon dioxide gas into the atmosphere during energy transfer? **(1 mark)**
- **A** biofuels
- **B** geothermal energy
- **C** tides
- **D** wind

3 Which of the following renewable energy resources is not dependent on the weather? **(1 mark)**
- **A** solar energy
- **B** hydroelectric power
- **C** tidal energy
- **D** wind power

4 Which of the following renewable energy resources does not make use of the Sun's energy? **(1 mark)**
- **A** solar energy
- **B** wave power
- **C** geothermal energy
- **D** wind power

5 Which of the following renewable energy resources is influenced by the Moon? **(1 mark)**
- **A** tidal energy
- **B** solar energy
- **C** geothermal energy
- **D** wind power

Score   / 5

Short-answer questions

1 Explain what is meant by 'renewable' and 'non-renewable' in the context of energy resources. (2 marks)

2 List three renewable energy resources and three non-renewable energy resources. (6 marks)

3 For each of the following types of renewable energy, state one possible disadvantage. (5 marks)

a) hydroelectric power

b) tidal power

c) solar energy

d) wind power

e) geothermal energy

Score   / 13

GCSE-style questions

Answer all parts of all questions. Continue on a separate sheet of paper if necessary.

1 Hydroelectric power stations can be used to store surplus energy during periods of low demand by pumping water back into the reservoir.

a) Explain how, during subsequent periods of high demand, hydroelectric power stations respond rapidly to meet energy requirements. **(3 marks)**

b) Describe the energy transfers that take place in a hydroelectric power station. **(2 marks)**

2 It is proposed to build a tidal barrage on a river estuary. The local population has mixed reactions to the proposal.

a) Suggest two reasons why some people may object to the proposal. **(2 marks)**

b) Suggest two reasons why some people may be in favour of the proposal. **(2 marks)**

3 ✎ Explain why the Sun can be considered to be the original energy source of most of our energy resources. Make reference to specific renewable and non-renewable resources in your answer. **(6 marks)**

Score   / 15

How well did you do?

| 0–10 | Try again | | 11–18 | Getting there | | 19–25 | Good work | | 26–33 | Excellent! |

For more information on this topic, see pages 46–47 of your Success Revision Guide.

Physics

Electrical Energy and Power

Multiple-choice questions

Choose just one answer: A, B, C or D.

1 Which of these formulae shows the relationship between energy and power? **(1 mark)**
- **A** power = current × voltage
- **B** energy = power × time
- **C** voltage = power + energy
- **D** $\text{current} = \dfrac{(\text{power} \times \text{time})}{\text{energy}}$

2 How much energy is converted at a power of 10 W in 10 s? **(1 mark)**
- **A** 100 J
- **B** 50 J
- **C** 200 J
- **D** 500 J

3 What is the power of a device that does 1000 J of work in 10 s? **(1 mark)**

- **A** 1000 W
- **B** 50 W
- **C** 100 W
- **D** 200 W

4 How long in seconds would it take to convert 80 000 J of energy at a power of 4 kW? **(1 mark)**
- **A** 100 s
- **B** 20 s
- **C** 200 s
- **D** 10 s

5 How many kWh of energy are converted by a device operating at 100 000 W for 30 minutes? **(1 mark)**
- **A** 50 kWh
- **B** 3333 kWh
- **C** 0.0003 kWh
- **D** 30 kWh

Score   / 5

Short-answer questions

1 How many joules equal 1 kWh? Give a calculation to support your answer.   (2 marks)

2 Calculate how many joules of electrical energy are converted by a 100 W bulb in 5 minutes. (2 marks)

3 State the standard unit used to measure each of the following, including the symbol.   (3 marks)

a) current .... **b)** voltage .... **c)** power ....

4 State three energy saving measures that your family could take to reduce the household electricity bills.   (3 marks)

Score   / 10

Answer all parts of all questions. Continue on a separate sheet of paper if necessary.

1 The European Union (EU) has banned the sale of 100 W filament bulbs because about 90 per cent of the input energy is wasted as heat. Instead, they are encouraging the use of more energy efficient bulb designs.

a) If electricity costs 10p a unit (kWh), how much would it cost to keep a 100 W light bulb on for 12 hours each day for a week? **(2 marks)**

....

....

b) The recommended replacement for a 100 W filament bulb is an 'energy saving' bulb with an efficiency of 56%.

i) Explain how a power rating of 18 W for the new design will give the same useful light output as the original bulb. Use calculations to support your answer. **(3 marks)**

....

....

....

ii) Calculate the cost per week, as in part **(a)** for operating the new bulb with a power rating of 18 W. **(2 marks)**

....

iii) Calculate how much money the new 18 W bulb would save per week. **(1 mark)**

....

c) ✎ Suggest whether you think the EU decision to ban 100 W bulbs and encourage the use of more energy efficient designs is the right thing to do. In your answer you should consider the environmental impact of such energy saving measures. You should also include a piece of information that you would need to know to make a more informed decision. **(6 marks)**

....

....

....

....

....

Score   / 14

Physics

How well did you do?

| 0–8 | Try again | 9–14 | Getting there | 15–21 | Good work | 22–29 | Excellent! |

For more information on this topic, see pages 48–49 of your Success Revision Guide.

47

Electricity Matters

Multiple-choice questions

Choose just one answer: A, B, C or D.

1 Which of the following statements is false? **(1 mark)**
- **A** a step-up transformer increases voltage
- **B** a step-up transformer decreases current
- **C** a step-up transformer increases current
- **D** a step-up transformer will only work with an alternating current

2 Which of the following statements is true? **(1 mark)**
- **A** transformers can change the power
- **B** transformers can do work
- **C** transformers are 100% efficient
- **D** transformers can change the value of an alternating current

3 Where is the voltage stepped-down in the UK National Grid? **(1 mark)**
- **A** power lines
- **B** pylons
- **C** power station
- **D** sub-station

4 Which of the following is NOT a disadvantage of nuclear power stations? **(1 mark)**
- **A** being at risk from terrorism
- **B** contribution to the greenhouse effect
- **C** accidental emission of radioactive waste
- **D** high decommissioning costs

5 Which of the following is NOT associated with nuclear power stations? **(1 mark)**
- **A** uranium
- **B** plutonium
- **C** carbon dioxide
- **D** radiation

Score   / 5

Short-answer questions

1 a) Fill in the missing words to complete the information about the National Grid. (5 marks)

The National Grid is the network that distributes .... power around the

country. It connects the power stations, where electricity is .... to the

users in homes and businesses. Electricity provided to the National Grid is generated

in such a way that the current .... The frequency at which this

happens is 50 Hz in the UK. The electricity reaches our homes via step-up transformers,

.... (often carried by overhead pylons), and .... transformers.

b) State one advantage and one disadvantage of the National Grid. (2 marks)

....

....

....

Score   / 7

Answer all parts of all questions. Continue on a separate sheet of paper if necessary.

1 Mains electricity is an alternating current. **(1 mark)**

   a) Describe what is meant by an 'alternating current'.

   b) One advantage of using an alternating current is that transformers can be used
   to increase or decrease the input voltage.

   i) Explain why we use step-up and step-down transformers in the National Grid. **(3 marks)**

   ii) Explain why transformers do not work on d.c. **(3 marks)**

2 A small power station supplies electricity at a voltage of 100 kV with a current of 50 A
into the National Grid:

   a) What is the power supplied by the generator? **(2 marks)**

   b) If this reaches domestic users at 230 V with a 10% power loss, what is the total
   useful power output? **(2 marks)**

   c) What is the total corresponding current supplied to users? **(2 marks)**

3 ✎ The UK government has recently taken the decision to increase the number of nuclear
   power stations providing power to the National Grid. The German government, in contrast,
   has taken the decision not to increase their nuclear power capability. By carefully
   evaluating the advantages and disadvantages of nuclear power, suggest which decision
   you are in agreement with. **(6 marks)**

   (Answer on a separate piece of paper.)

Physics

Score   / 19

How well did you do?

| 0–9 | Try again | 10–17 | Getting there | 18–24 | Good work | 25–31 | Excellent! |

For more information on this topic, see pages 50–51 of your Success Revision Guide.

Particles and Heat Transfer

Multiple-choice questions

Choose just one answer: A, B, C or D.

1 What is the only method by which heat can be transferred through a vacuum? **(1 mark)**
- **A** conduction
- **B** convection
- **C** evaporation
- **D** radiation

2 Which of the following surfaces would best absorb infrared radiation? **(1 mark)**
- **A** dark and matt
- **B** dark and shiny
- **C** light and matt
- **D** light and shiny

3 Which of the following statements about specific heat capacity (SHC) is not true? **(1 mark)**
- **A** SHC can be calculated if energy, mass and temperature change are known
- **B** SHC is the same for all materials
- **C** SHC is measured in J/kg/°C
- **D** SHC is the energy needed to increase the temperature of 1 kg of a material by 1°C

4 Which physical state is best for conducting energy? **(1 mark)**
- **A** gas
- **B** liquid
- **C** solid
- **D** fluid

5 Which of the following materials is the best heat conductor? **(1 mark)**
- **A** water
- **B** metal
- **C** gas
- **D** wool

Score / 5

Short-answer questions

1 Compared to some materials, water requires a relatively large amount of energy to bring about a temperature rise. The specific heat capacity of water is 4200 J/kg/°C.

a) Calculate how much heat energy would be required to bring 200 g of water in a kettle at 20°C to the boil. **(2 marks)**

....

....

b) Calculate the energy required to warm up 25 kg of bath water at 10°C to a temperature of 20°C. **(2 marks)**

....

....

c) Explain why water is chosen as the coolant in many heat exchangers. **(2 marks)**

....

....

Score / 6

Answer all parts of all questions. Continue on a separate sheet of paper if necessary.

1 In an experiment to investigate heat transfer, four different coloured (but otherwise identical) boxes of boiling water are allowed to cool for 3 minutes. The following results are obtained:

Colour of box	Final temp. (°C)
Silver	80
Matt black	60
White	75
Shiny black	70

a) What is the initial temperature of all the boxes? (1 mark)

....

b) Explain why it is important that the initial temperature of the water, the size and shape of the box and the amount of water in each box are the same. (2 marks)

....

....

c) Which box has... (2 marks)

i) cooled the most? .... **ii)** cooled the least? ....

d) Explain these observations, referring in your answer to the possible contributions of conduction, convection and radiation as mechanisms of heat transfer. (4 marks)

....

....

....

....

e) Suggest another factor that you would consider in order to improve the reliability of the results. (1 mark)

....

....

Score   / 10

How well did you do?

| 0–5 | Try again | 6–11 | Getting there | 12–17 | Good work | 18–21 | Excellent! |

For more information on this topic, see pages 52–53 of your Success Revision Guide.

Physics

Describing Waves

Multiple-choice questions

Choose just one answer, A, B, C or D.

1 For which type of wave are the oscillations parallel to the direction in which the wave travels? **(1 mark)**
   A transverse
   B longitudinal
   C electromagnetic
   D water

2 Which of the following formulae correctly calculates the speed of a wave? **(1 mark)**
   A wavelength x frequency
   B frequency x amplitude
   C $\dfrac{\text{wavelength}}{\text{amplitude}}$
   D $\dfrac{\text{frequency}}{\text{wavelength}}$

3 What is the highest point on a transverse wave called? **(1 mark)**
   A compression
   B trough
   C amplitude
   D crest

4 Sound is an example of which type of wave? **(1 mark)**
   A longitudinal
   B seismic
   C electromagnetic
   D transverse

5 What is the lowest point on a transverse wave? **(1 mark)**
   A rarefaction point
   B trough
   C oscillation
   D crest

Score   / 5

Short-answer questions

1 Calculate the wavelength of water waves of frequency 2 Hz travelling at 20 cm/s.   (2 marks)

2 Calculate how far a sound wave of wavelength 34 cm and frequency 1000 Hz will travel in 5 s.   (2 marks)

3 True or false?   True   False   (3 marks)

   A Amplitude is measured from the top of the crest to the bottom of the trough.   ☐   ☐

   B The distance from one crest to the next crest is a wavelength.   ☐   ☐

   C Wavelength is the total length of a series of waves from the first crest to the last crest.   ☐   ☐

Score   / 7

GCSE-style questions

Answer all parts of all questions. Continue on a separate sheet of paper if necessary.

1 Harry is listening to music on his MP3 player. The electrical signal from the player is fed to the headphones in order to produce the sound that Harry hears.

a) Complete the following passage, inserting words into the spaces or choosing from the options provided. **(4 marks)**

The sound that Harry hears is due to .... in the air produced by the headphones.

Electrical .... is transferred to the air particles to create a sound wave. Sound is an example of a **transverse / longitudinal** wave, in which the air particles move in a direction **parallel / perpendicular** to the direction of wave travel.

b) The diagram alongside shows a transverse wave, such as a water wave. It could also be taken to represent the electrical signal producing a steady tone in Harry's headphones.

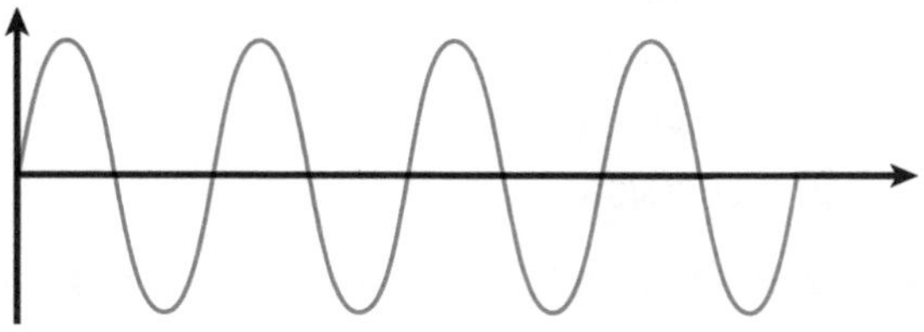

On the diagram label the following features:
i) amplitude **ii)** wavelength. **(2 marks)**

c) i) State how the wave would differ if it was to show an electrical signal producing a quieter sound in the headphones. **(1 mark)**

....

ii) State how the wave would differ if it was to show an electrical signal producing a sound of higher pitch. **(1 mark)**

....

d) Explain why the diagram is not a good representation of the sound wave that is produced by the headphones. **(3 marks)**

....

....

....

e) Although the wave shown does not directly represent sound it can nevertheless be a useful model if it is used to show how the air pressure rather than displacement changes.

Now complete the following continuation of the paragraph in part **a)**. **(3 marks)**

The sound wave consists of alternating high and low pressure regions. Areas of high pressure are known as **compressions / rarefactions**. Areas of low pressure are called **compressions / rarefactions**. In a sound of lower pitch the compressions occur **closer together / further apart**. In a sound of greater volume the **amplitude / frequency** is higher.

Score /14

How well did you do?

0–6	Try again	7–12	Getting there	13–19	Good work	20–26	Excellent!

For more information on this topic, see pages 54–55 of your Success Revision Guide.

Wave Behaviour

Multiple-choice questions

Choose just one answer: A, B, C or D.

1 What is the correct term for the change of direction, that accompanies a change in speed, when a wave travels from one medium to another? **(1 mark)**
A reflection
B refraction
C diffraction
D dispersion

2 Which term refers to the change in direction, without a change in speed, when a wave hits a suitable surface? **(1 mark)**
A refraction
B incidence
C reflection
D an echo

3 When a wave strikes a surface, the angle between the wave's direction of travel and the normal is called the angle of: **(1 mark)**
A incidence
B approach
C refraction
D reflection

4 Which colour of light is refracted the most by a prism? **(1 mark)**
A red
B green
C blue
D violet

5 Which term means 'the spreading of waves when going through a narrow gap'? **(1 mark)**
A refraction
B diffraction
C reflection
D dispersion

Score   / 5

Short-answer questions

1 The following ray diagram showing the reflection of a beam of light contains an error.

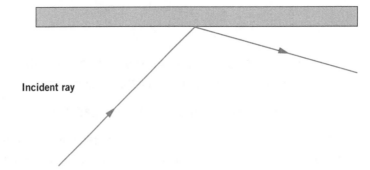

Incident ray

a) Circle the part of the diagram with the error. (1 mark)

b) Draw on the diagram to show how the error should be corrected. (1 mark)

c) Complete the following statement. (1 mark)

When a wave is reflected, the angle of reflection...

Score   / 3

GCSE-style questions

Answer all parts of all questions. Continue on a separate sheet of paper if necessary.

1 When you look into a body of water from above, it is very difficult to accurately judge distances beneath the surface of the water.

a) Explain why the bottom of a swimming pool appears to be closer, i.e. the pool seems shallower, than it really is. Draw a ray diagram to support your answer. **(3 marks)**

b) Describe why the same difficulties would not be faced by an observer who is underwater. **(2 marks)**

2 Colin is walking down the road towards a T-junction. He can hear the sound of approaching sirens, but he only sees the police car when it speeds by the end of the road.

Explain why it is possible to hear sounds but not see around the corner. **(3 marks)**

3 When sound waves hit a surface they can be reflected. In everyday language, this is known as an echo. A battleship floating on the surface of the ocean makes use of this behaviour by using a sonar detector to locate underwater objects, such as submarines. It does this by recording the time taken to 'hear' the echo. If ultrasonic waves at a frequency of 30 kHz travel through the water at 1500 m/s and the detector receives the signals after a delay of 0.5 s, calculate the following:

a) the wavelength of the sonar waves. **(2 marks)**

b) the distance to the submarine. **(2 marks)**

Score   / 12

How well did you do?

| 0–5 | Try again | 6–11 | Getting there | 12–16 | Good work | 17–20 | Excellent! |

For more information on this topic, see pages 56–57 of your Success Revision Guide.

Seismic Waves and the Earth

Multiple-choice questions

Choose just one answer, A, B, C or D.

1 Which seismic waves travel fastest? **(1 mark)**
- **A** earthquake waves
- **B** S-waves
- **C** P-waves
- **D** tectonic waves

2 Which seismic waves are longitudinal? **(1 mark)**
- **A** P-waves
- **B** earthquake waves
- **C** S-waves
- **D** tectonic waves

3 S-waves waves are: **(1 mark)**
- **A** longitudinal
- **B** transverse

- **C** primary
- **D** sound

4 What is the name for the outermost layer of the Earth? **(1 mark)**
- **A** core
- **B** magma
- **C** crust
- **D** mantle

5 In which layer of the Earth are the rocks semi-molten? **(1 mark)**
- **A** magma
- **B** crust
- **C** core
- **D** mantle

Score / 5

Short-answer questions

1 Fill in the missing words to explain the behaviour of P-waves and S-waves. (7 marks)

When an earthquake occurs, waves spread from the site of the quake throughout the Earth. These

waves are called .... waves, of which there are two types: P-waves and S-waves. The

.... -waves travel fastest and are the first to be detected. They are ....

pressure waves that are capable of travelling through both solid and .... materials.

The .... -waves are detected later because they are unable to travel through

.... parts of the Earth. Monitoring this wave activity using pieces of equipment called

.... allows scientists to analyse the Earth's inner structure.

2 State which currents in the mantle of the Earth cause the continental tectonic plates to move. (1 mark)

....

3 State two pieces of evidence that support Wegener's theory of continental drift. (2 marks)

....

....

....

Score / 10

Answer all parts of all questions. Continue on a separate sheet of paper if necessary.

1 A scientist in an earthquake monitoring station obtains the following reading on a seismometer.

a) On the seismograph, label
i) the P-waves ii) the S-waves. (2 marks)

b) The scientist uses the following formula to estimate the distance of the earthquake from the monitoring station:

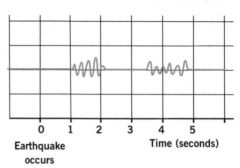

Distance from station (km) =

(Time for S-waves to arrive (s) – Time for P-waves to arrive (s)) x 8

Use the seismograph and formula to estimate the distance of the earthquake from the monitoring station. (2 marks)

....

....

c) For the same earthquake, some other stations only picked up readings for one set of waves on their seismometers.

i) Describe where these stations are likely to be located in relation to the epicentre of the earthquake. (1 mark)

....

ii) What is the name given to the region in which these stations are located?
Tick the correct option.

A Safe haven ☐
B Shadow zone ☐
C Refraction region ☐
D Seismic area ☐

d) Explain how understanding how P-waves and S-waves behave has also helped scientists to develop a better understanding of the structure of the Earth. (3 marks)

....

....

....

Score / 8

Physics

How well did you do?

| 0–6 | Try again | 7–12 | Getting there | 13–17 | Good work | 18–23 | Excellent! |

For more information on this topic, see pages 58–59 of your Success Revision Guide.

The Electromagnetic Spectrum

Multiple-choice questions

Choose just one answer: A, B, C or D.

❶ Which is the longest wavelength region of the electromagnetic spectrum? **(1 mark)**
- **A** light
- **B** radio
- **C** X-ray
- **D** infrared

❷ Which part of the spectrum has a wavelength slightly greater than that of visible light? **(1 mark)**
- **A** X-ray
- **B** microwave
- **C** light
- **D** infrared

❸ Which of the following wavelengths falls into the spectrum of visible light? **(1 mark)**

- **A** 3×10^2
- **B** 4×10^{-2}
- **C** 5×10^{-7}
- **D** 6×10^{-12}

❹ Which of these is NOT a possible effect of radiation absorption? **(1 mark)**
- **A** the material heats up
- **B** atoms in the material are ionised
- **C** chemical reactions are more likely to occur
- **D** the material cools down

❺ Which electromagnetic waves are sometimes known as heat radiation? **(1 mark)**
- **A** light
- **B** radio
- **C** X-ray
- **D** infrared

Score / 5

Short-answer questions

❶ **a)** Underline the correct words to complete this description of the electromagnetic spectrum. (3 marks)

The electromagnetic spectrum is **continuous / intermittent** from the longest to shortest wavelengths.

All electromagnetic waves are **longitudinal / transverse** and travel through space at a speed of **300 / 300 000 / 300 000 000** m/s.

b) Put the following regions of the electromagnetic spectrum in the correct order, starting with the longest wavelength. (7 marks)

radio waves, X-rays, visible light, gamma rays, microwaves, infrared, ultraviolet

....

❷ Many conventional diagrams showing the electromagnetic spectrum can be misleading when it comes to the shortest wavelengths, i.e. gamma rays and X-rays.

Explain why this is. (2 marks)

....

....

Score / 12

Answer all parts of all questions. Continue on a separate sheet of paper if necessary.

1 Radiation from all parts of the electromagnetic spectrum travels through space at the 'speed of light' which is 300 000 km/s.

   a) Calculate the frequency of microwaves of wavelength 2 cm.   **(2 marks)**

   b) Calculate the wavelength of ultraviolet light of frequency 6×10^{15} Hz.   **(2 marks)**

   c) The following data is found on a radio-mast: 'Range of frequencies is 300 kHZ to 500 MHz'.

      i) Calculate the corresponding range of wavelengths.   **(2 marks)**

      ii) The optimum length for a mast is usually one quarter of a wavelength. State how long you would make the mast for optimum performance.   **(1 mark)**

2 **a)** Describe what is meant by 'intensity' in reference to radiation striking a surface.   **(1 mark)**

   b) State two ways in which intensity can be increased.   **(2 marks)**

   c) The energy in electromagnetic radiation is arranged in 'packets' called photons. The photon energy is directly proportional to the frequency.

   In a photographic dark room, the photographer processes film that is extremely light sensitive. With reference to photon energy, explain why red lights can be used in dark rooms but other coloured lights cannot.   **(3 marks)**

Score   / 13

Physics

How well did you do?

| 0–8 | Try again | 9–14 | Getting there | 15–22 | Good work | 23–30 | Excellent! |

For more information on this topic, see pages 60–61 of your Success Revision Guide.

Light, Radio Waves and Microwaves

Multiple-choice questions

Choose just one answer: A, B, C or D.

1 Which of the following radiations does NOT reach the Earth's surface from the Sun? **(1 mark)**
- **A** microwaves
- **B** high energy infrared
- **C** visible light
- **D** low energy ultraviolet

2 Which of the following is NOT a property of radio waves and microwaves? **(1 mark)**
- **A** they are reflected by metal surfaces
- **B** they can have a heating effect
- **C** they have an ionising effect
- **D** they have much greater wavelengths than visible light

3 Medium wave radio signals travel long distances by reflection from a layer of charged particles called the: **(1 mark)**

- **A** atmosphere
- **B** stratosphere
- **C** heliosphere
- **D** ionosphere

4 Microwaves can be used for cooking. What is the purpose of the metal grid on the door of a microwave oven? **(1 mark)**
- **A** to help heat the food
- **B** to increase the microwave intensity
- **C** to prevent microwaves from getting out of the oven
- **D** to produce the microwaves

5 Plants rely on the energy from visible light for: **(1 mark)**
- **A** respiration
- **B** photosynthesis
- **C** digestion
- **D** transmission

Score / 5

Short-answer questions

1 When a radio signal is broadcast, an alternating current of electrons in the transmitter aerial causes the radio wave to be emitted. Describe what happens to the electrons in the receiver aerial when the radio signal is detected. (1 mark)

2 a) State why the casing of a microwave oven has to be opaque to the waves. (1 mark)

b) Explain why a microwave oven is good for cooking a ready meal, but not for making toast. (2 marks)

3 Fill in the missing words to complete the following passage. (3 marks)

Detection of light by a camera is similar to how the eye detects light. In both, light passes through a small hole to produce a small, upside down .... A .... is used to gather and focus more light. The photographic film or digital screen inside the camera plays the role of the .... in the eye.

Score / 7

Answers

Abbreviations used

;	separates marking points
ORA	or reverse argument
OWTTE	or words to that effect

For questions marked ✐, where marks are awarded for the quality of written communication, model answers have been provided. The model answers would score the full 6 marks available. If you have made most of the points given in the model answer and communicated your ideas clearly, in a logical sequence with few errors in spelling, punctuation and grammar, you would get 6 marks. You will lose marks if some of the points are missing, if the answer lacks clarity or if there are serious errors in spelling, punctuation and grammar.

BIOLOGY

Pages 4–5 A Balanced Diet
Multiple-choice questions
1. B 2. D 3. A 4. C 5. C
Short-answer questions
1. a) false b) true c) false d) false
2. **Any four from:** age; gender; level of activity; vegetarian; food allergy.
GCSE-style questions
1. a) A balanced diet needs the <u>correct</u> amount of each of the seven food types.
   b) first class proteins/essential amino acids
2. fatty acids; glycerol; store; mineral; haemoglobin; scurvy; cellulose; constipation.
3. a) $0.6 \times 60 = 36$ g of protein
   b) EAR will increase, as body mass is increasing; Protein is needed for growth of the developing baby; More carbohydrate and fat will be needed to supply energy.

Pages 6–7 Homeostasis
Multiple-choice questions
1. B 2. D 3. A 4. A 5. C
Short-answer questions
1.

Diabetes	Caused by	Treated by
Type 1	pancreas fails to make insulin	insulin injections
Type 2	body cells fail to respond to insulin	controlling diet (less carbohydrate)

2. Receptors; Gland secretes hormone; Bloodstream transports hormone; Target organ.
GCSE-style questions
1. Homeostasis is the control of the internal environment; to keep it constant; e.g. temperature, water, sugar content, mineral content.
2. a) allow 0.1–0.15 b) eaten a meal
   c) allow 30–50 mins d) type 1
   e) Glucagon; is released from the pancreas; and targets the liver; Glycogen is converted back to glucose; so the blood sugar level is returned to normal.
3. Negative feedback is a control mechanism that detects a change from the normal level; and brings about a response to return it to normal. (OWTTE) For example, the thermostat in a house detects the room temperature if it is too high it turns the boiler/radiators off, so the room cools down.

Pages 8–9 Hormones and Reproduction
Multiple-choice questions
1. B 2. C 3. D 4. A 5. D
Short-answer questions
1. a) oestrogen and progesterone b) FSH
   c) pituitary gland
2. secondary; testosterone; oestrogen; sperm; egg/ovum

GCSE-style questions
1.

Male	Female
voice breaks	hips widen
muscle development	breasts develops
pubic hair/hair on chest/underarms/face	pubic hair/hair underarms

2. a) 4 days b) oestrogen c) LH
   d) oestrogen and progesterone
   e) i) Fertilisation has occured. The woman is pregnant.
      ii) Progesterone is produced; by the placenta.
3. ✐ One cause of infertility in women is when their body does not release eggs from the ovaries. This can be treated using a fertility drug, which contains hormones similar to FSH. The drugs stimulate the production and release of eggs. Women treated by this method sometimes release a number of eggs each month. *(Or description of how fertility drugs and IVF can be used to help women with blocked fallopian tubes become pregnant.)*

Pages 10–11 Responding to the Environment
Multiple-choice questions
1. A 2. C 3. C 4. C 5. B
Short-answer questions
1. cornea – main site of refraction; pupil – allows light to enter the eye; lens – refraction of light for fine focussing; retina – contains the photoreceptors; iris – changes the size of the pupil; optic nerve – transmits electrical impulse to CNS; ciliary muscle – changes the shape of the lens
2. a) rods; and cones b) cones
GCSE-style questions
1. A cornea B lens C ciliary muscle D retina
2.

Object	Ciliary muscle	Suspensory ligament	Lens shape	Light refracted
Distant	~~contracted~~ / relaxed	tight / ~~slack~~	~~fatter~~ / thinner	a little / ~~a lot~~

3. ✐ A change in the environment is called a stimulus. The stimuli are detected by receptors in the sense organs. Messages are transmitted from the receptors and along nerve cells (neurones) in the form of electrical impulses. All the information is coordinated by the central nervous system (CNS), which is made up of the brain and spinal cord. This sends messages to the appropriate muscle or gland, which acts as an effector and brings about a response.

Pages 12–13 The Nervous System
Multiple-choice questions
1. A 2 B 3. C 4. A 5. D
Short-answer questions
1. a) sensory neurone
   b) A myelin sheath B nucleus C cell body D axon
2. a) false b) true c) false
GCSE-style questions
1. axon carries impulse a long distance; myelin sheath insulates impulse so that it travels faster; dendrites cover larger area/allows several cells to respond to impulse
2.

C	A	B	D

3. ✐ When pain receptors in the skin detect the stimulus (pin prick), an electrical impulse is transmitted along the sensory neurone. The impulse passes across a synapse to the relay neurone and then onto a motor neurone. The motor neurone carries the impulse to the effector.

In this case the effector is a muscle, which contracts, pulling the finger away from the source of pain. This pathway allows the body to respond very quickly.

Pages 14–15 Plant Responses
Multiple-choice questions
1. C 2 D 3. B 4. A 5. D
Short-answer questions
1. a) phototropism b) geotropism c) auxin
2. a)–c) **Any three from:** Kill broad leaf weeds; produce seedless fruit; control fruit ripening; produce plants from cuttings; control seed germination.
GCSE-style questions
1. a) They bend towards the light.
   b) Auxin travels down the shoots to the shaded side; It causes cell elongation to occur on this side; so the shoots bend.
2. ✐ When a plant is placed on its side, auxin gathers on the underside due to gravity. In the roots, the auxin inhibits the growth of cells, so the upper side grows faster than the underside, causing the root to grow downwards in the direction of gravity. This is called positive geotropism. In the shoots, the auxin causes more growth on the underside, which does not receive any light, so the shoot bends upwards towards the light. This is called positive phototropism.
3. It is negatively geotropic/positively phototropic.

Pages 16–17 Pathogens and Infections
Multiple-choice questions
1. C 2. A 3. C 4. C 5. C
Short-answer questions
1. fungi/virus; bacteria/protozoa; infectious; virus; air; antigens; white blood/lymphocyte; antibodies; complementary.
2. **Any three from:** Mucus traps dirt and pathogens in nose and respiratory system; Cilia are tiny hairs that line the airways pushing the mucus up so it can be swallowed; Stomach acid kills bacteria on food; Tears contain lysozymes, which kill bacteria.
GCSE-style questions
1. a) protozoa
   b) transmitted by mosquitoes (animal vector); biting humans
   c) insect repellents; insect nets; draining swamps.
2. a) Antigens are proteins found on the surface of pathogens (cells); Antibodies are produced by white blood cells, they have a complementary shape to the pathogen's antigens
   b) Lymphocytes produce antibodies; Phagocytes engulf pathogens.
3. a false b) false c) true d) false
4. a) Phagocytes engulf bacteria; and then digestive enzymes break them down.
   b) An immune response occurred/the white blood cells produced antibodies; memory cells were also produced; memory cells live for many years in the body; and produce antibodies rapidly.

Pages 18–19 Antibiotics and Antiseptics
Multiple-choice questions
1. B 2. C 3. B 4. A 5. B
Short-answer questions
1. a) agar
   b) energy source (carbohydrate); and nutrients e.g. protein, minerals and vitamins.
   c) **Any two from:** aseptic techniques, e.g. sterilise inoculating loop; sterilise Petri dish; keep covered.
2. antibiotics; disinfectant; antiseptic; antiseptic
GCSE-style questions
1. a) Agar provides a medium for growth and nutrients.
   b) Antibiotics are specific to certain bacteria (OWTTE)
   c) C; biggest no bacterial growth area

d) Any one from: penicillin; streptomycin.

2. **a)** Mutation occurs.
   b) Complete the course of antibiotics; do not use to treat viral infections.
   c) Any three from: Hospital visitors and staff to wash hands with alcohol gel; disinfectant surfaces (floors, tables); use different antibiotics; advise patients to complete the course.

Pages 20–21 Vaccinations
Multiple-choice questions
1. D   **2.** C   **3.** B   **4.** A   **5.** B
Short-answer questions
1. **a)** true   **b)** true   **c)** true   **d)** false   **e)** true
2. Vaccines contain certain antigens; White blood cells produce antibodies only for those antigens.
GCSE-style questions
1. **a)** If they are already suffering from the disease to give quicker protection.
   b) This immunity is passive; No memory cells are produced so the protection doesn't last long.
2. ✎ Active immunity brings about an immune response. The white blood cells detect the antigens (pathogen) and produce antibodies. Due to memory cells, the protection last a lifetime as the body can quickly produce the antibodies, if the same antigens are detected again. Passive immunity involves antibodies being given, for example as an injection or in mother's milk, so the white blood cells are not involved. This brings about rapid but short-lived protection.
3. **a)** measles; mumps; rubella.
   b) Rubella can cause brain damage in the baby.
   c) Any two from: MMR protects against potentially fatal diseases; Increase in these diseases if vaccination not given; Links to autism gave parents concerns, although now these have been discredited; All vaccines may result in side effects.
4. Flu virus reproduces rapidly so high mutation rate; Antigens are therefore constantly changing so different from those in the previous year's vaccine.

Pages 22–23 Drugs
Multiple-choice questions
1. A   **2.** A   **3.** D   **4.** A   **5.** C
Short-answer questions
1. **a)** Addictive – want more even though it may have harmful effects.
   b) Tolerance – need a greater quantity to achieve the same effect.
2. **a)** Babies were born with severe limb abnormalities.
   b) leprosy
3. **a)** false   **b)** true   **c)** false
GCSE-style questions
1. **a)** to make sure it is safe; and that it works
   b) It is first tested on human cells and microorganisms; then on animals and finally there will be human trials.
   c) Cruel to animals; Animals are different to humans, so effects are different.
2. **a)** A placebo looks like the drug but has no effect on the body; It is given for comparison to test that the drug does make a difference.
   b) The patients do not know if they are taking the drug or a placebo.
   c) The results are more reliable as the patients haven't influenced them.
   d) Any one from: test more patients; double blind test
3. Stimulants cause more neurotransmitters to be released; Depressants block the neurotransmitters.

Pages 24–25 Genes and Chromosomes
Multiple-choice questions
1. A   **2.** B   **3.** A   **4.** D   **5.** B
Short-answer questions
1. gene   codes for a protein
   DNA   chemical containing four different bases
   chromosome   structure found in the nucleus
2. **a)** deoxyribonucleic acid   **b)** A,T,G,C
3. 46; gametes; zygote

GCSE-style questions
1. **a)**

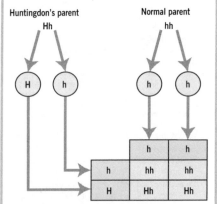

(1 mark for each: correct parental genotypes; gametes; offspring genotype)
   b) 0.5/50%
2. Inherit half our genes from our mother; the other half from our father.
3. examples might include:

Cause of variation	Examples
genetic/inherited	1. eye colour 2. nose shape
environmental	1. scars 2. language spoken

Pages 26–27 Passing on Genes
Multiple-choice questions
1. A   **2.** B   **3.** B   **4.** A   **5.** D
Short-answer questions
1. recessive   Allele only shown in characteristic if two are inherited.
   homozygous   The two alleles inherited for a gene are the same.
   genotype   Alleles an organism carries.
   phenotype   Characteristics expressed.
2.

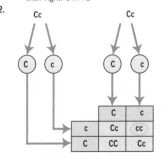

(1 mark for each: correct parental genotypes; gametes; offspring genotype)
GCSE-style questions
1. **a)** Advantage – identify if unborn child has the genetic disease
   Disadvantage – not always reliable/risk of miscarriage
   b) Parents could decide to have a termination; Some people consider this manslaughter/not their right. OWTTE
2.

(1 mark for each: correct parental genotypes; gametes; offspring genotype; Probability = 0.25/25%)
3. **a)** recessive
   b) Any two from: feeling tired; cold hands and feet; pain in joints; lungs and bones

---

4. **a)** Both parents are non-sufferers; but must be carriers of cystic fibrosis as John has cystic fibrosis; He must inherit a recessive allele from each parent.
   b) homozygous (recessive)
   c) Any two from: thick mucus; breathing difficulties; chest infections; digestive problems.

Pages 28–29 Gene Technology
Multiple-choice questions
1. A   **2.** C   **3.** A   **4.** D   **5.** D
Short-answer questions
1. **a)** body cell
   b) So that Dolly did not have too much genetic information.
   c) Sheep A; the genetic information came from this sheep.
GCSE-style questions
1. Cutting dipped in rooting powder and placed in soil; Tissue culture involves growing a small group of cells in a lab; and then transferring the individual plantlets to greenhouses.
2.

C	A	B	E	D

3. **a)** Stem cells are unspecialised cells and can divide to make different tissues.
   b) Doctors can use stem cells to repair damaged tissue/grow new organs.
4. They develop from the same egg and sperm; They contain the same genetic information.
5. **a) Any two from:** pest resistant; resistant to herbicides; higher yield
   b) For – more food to supply starving populations; less use of harmful insecticides
   Against – **Any two from:** human against God/nature; health problems; may pollinate wild crops

Pages 30–31 Evolution and Natural Selection
Multiple-choice questions
1. C   **2.** A   **3.** A   **4.** C   **5.** C
Short-answer questions
1. gradual change in a species; over a long period of time
2. natural selection
   a) large   b) remain constant
   c) variation   d) inherited
GCSE-style questions
1. **Any two from:** Discovery of genes; coding for inherited characteristics; Genes can not be changed by the environment.
2. Organism does not adapt to changing conditions/environment so does not have a selective advantage; It may be more likely to be eaten by predators (as slower/not camouflaged), so less chance to reproduce and population numbers rapidly decrease.
3. **a)** Trees covered in soot; so dark colour are better camouflaged and less likely to be eaten.
   b) mutation
   c) Dark peppered moths have a selective advantage; so are less likely to be eaten (better camouflaged); They have more chance of reproducing; and passing on the darker colour gene to their offspring.

Pages 32–33 Competition and Adaptation
Multiple-choice questions
1. A   **2.** D   **3.** B   **4.** B   **5.** C
Short-answer questions
1. habitat; compete; intraspecific; interspecific; adaptations; population
2. camouflage   binocular vision   monocular vision
   pointed canine teeth   thorns
GCSE-style questions
1.

owl	velvety down feathers	silent flight
wolf	sharp teeth	for ripping meat
rabbit	binocular vision	to give better vision of predators
seal	layer of thick blubber beneath the skin	to keep warm
clownfish	striped colouring	camouflage against the reef

2. **Any two from:** Live born animals are more likely to survive than eggs; predators may eat some eggs before they hatch; eggs may not all hatch due to the weather; there is limited room inside organisms for babies to develop.

3. ✎ Mice and elephants are both warm-blooded animals, so they need to generate a lot of heat to maintain their body temperature. Elephants are much larger animals than mice and have a smaller surface area to volume ratio. This means they lose less heat to their surroundings and need to respire less to produce heat energy. Therefore, they need less food than a mouse relative to their body mass. In addition to this, mice generally live in cooler climates and are active at night, when temperatures are lower. This increases the amount of heat lost to the surroundings and the need to respire, thus increasing the need for food.

Pages 34–35 Energy Flow
Multiple-choice questions
1. D   2. A   3. B   4. C   5. C
Short-answer questions
1. Birds and mammals are homeothermic (warm-blooded), so lose more heat energy keeping warm.
2. biomass; energy; trophic; energy; water; energy; dry; dead; more
GCSE-style questions
1. Less energy is used in movement and wasted as heat loss; so a greater % of the food given to the animal by the farmer is turned into biomass.
2. a) Fish consumed some of the DDT in the water but not enough to kill them; the fish themselves were then consumed by the grebes, who got more poison than individual fish did because they ate more than one fish; the poison accumulated in their bodies because it is hard for the body to break it down; the grebes consumed enough to kill them.
   b) a link between two factors (variables)
   c) toxicology / autopsy report on the dead grebes (and fish); samples of water taken from the affected area; statements from farmers as to the use of DDT
3. Barn owls only eat dormice; foxes eat more than one type of food.

Pages 36–37 Recycling
Multiple-choice questions
1. A   2. B   3. A   4. C   5. A
Short-answer questions
1. **Any three from:** respiration; weathering of limestone; decomposition by bacteria; combustion (burning).
2. A combustion; B respiration; C photosynthesis; D death; E feeding; F decomposition (or respiration in decomposers)
GCSE-style questions
1. a) nitrogen-fixing bacteria
   b) nitrogen is insoluble; and unreactive
   c) fixes nitrogen to provide nitrates in the soil
2. a) Up to 40°C an increase in the temperature increases the rate of decay; 40°C is the fastest rate of decay *(by these decomposers – although other decomposers may work at different temperatures)*; at temperatures above 40°C, the rate drops dramatically until no further decay can happen.
   b) In the first part of the graph the increase in rate of reaction is due to more frequent successful collisions of molecules due to increased temperature; after the peak rate, the increase in energy serves to denature the enzymes involved in the reaction, which means the rate of reaction drops suddenly.
   c) Decay by bacteria releases heat in respiration; the build up of heat would kill the bacteria/denature the enzymes in the bacteria; turning the compost heap releases the heat which has built up.
3. Minerals would remain trapped in the dead bodies of plants and animals and would not be available for new growth.

Pages 38–39 Populations and Pollution
Multiple-choice questions
1. C   2. C   3. A   4. C   5. C

Short-answer questions
1.
Pollutants	Problems they cause
carbon dioxide	the greenhouse effect
fertilisers & sewage	polluted rivers and lakes
heavy metals	accumulates in food chains
domestic waste	landfill sites releasing gases

2. a) skin cancer   b) CFCs   c) **Any one from:** fridges; aerosols
GCSE-style questions
1. ✎ The greenhouse effect is caused by a build-up of gases, such as carbon dioxide and methane, in the upper atmosphere. These gases allow radiation from the Sun to enter the atmosphere. However, they prevent radiation from being reflected back into space, and they trap infrared radiation from the Earth. This leads to a gradual increase in temperature of the Earth, which is called 'Global Warming'.
2. unpredictable weather conditions; increased drought in some areas; increased risk of flooding in some places; ice caps melting; expansion of the oceans due to increased volume of water at higher temperatures; changes to habitat due to the climate change; possible extinction/endangerment of some species due to their not being able to cope with the climate change.
3. a) (as time goes on) there is an increase in the number of people getting skin cancer; and the amount of ozone (in the atmosphere) falls
   b) UV causes skin cancer; ozone absorbs/filters UV
   c) No; from 1970–1975 the amount of ozone goes up but the number of people suffering from skin cancer also goes up.
4. a) acid rain
   b) it is soluble in water (to form an acid)
5. Fertilisers run off the land into watercourses where they increase algal growth; which blocks the light to plants below the surface of the water restricting photosynthesis for the plants here; these plants die; bacteria decompose their bodies; this leads to putrification of the water; bacteria use up all the available oxygen; aquatic animals can no longer survive in the water.

PHYSICS

Pages 40–41 The Electricity Supply
Multiple-choice questions
1. B   2. C   3. D   4. A   5. C
Short-answer questions
1. a)

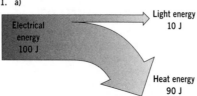

Electrical energy 100 J → Light energy 10 J; Heat energy 90 J

   b) i) electrical ii) light iii) heat
2. $\frac{8.4}{24} \times 100 = 35\%$

(1 mark for calculation; 1 mark for answer)
GCSE-style questions
1. a) Passive solar cells use the heat from the sun to directly heat water; active solar cells transfer solar energy to electrical energy.
   b) **Advantages may include:** domestic solar panels can save on electricity bills; 'clean' energy.
      Disadvantages may include: expensive to install; UK weather unreliable.
   c) Efficiency is a measure of the amount of useful energy (electricity) produced from the total energy input.
   d) $\frac{310}{1000} \times 100 = 31\%$
   e) i) Energy is not destroyed, it is converted / transferred into different forms.
      ii) During the transfer process, some energy is wasted in 'non-useful' forms; such as heat energy and kinetic energy.
   f) **Answers may include:** increasing efficiency of energy transfer (e.g. in solar cells); reducing

construction / installation costs; government initiatives to encourage use of renewable energy over fossil fuels.

Pages 42–43 Generating Electricity
Multiple-choice questions
1. A   2. D   3. C   4. B   5. D
Short-answer questions
1. a) A Furnace   B Turbine   C Generator   D Transformer   E Pylon / National Grid.
   b) i) Turbines allow water, steam or air to drive around the blades; turning the kinetic energy of the moving water, steam or air into rotational kinetic energy of the turbine to turn the generator.
      ii) Generators convert kinetic energy to electrical energy.
   c) They have formed over millennia from the decayed remains of pre-historic plants and animals.
GCSE-style questions
1. a) i) Biofuels produce carbon dioxide emissions when they are burned.
      ii) **Answers may include:** because biofuels are carbon neutral; they produce carbon dioxide emissions when burned but these are balanced / offset by growing plants to produce the biofuels; because the plants photosynthesise and remove carbon dioxide from the atmosphere.
      iii) **Any two from:** wood; straw; manure; sugar.
   b) **Answers may include:** availability of fuel; availability of water; impact on local environment; local infrastructure (roads, etc.); access by emergency services.
   c) voltage; rotates; changing.
   d) **Answers may include:** safety of plant / workers; radiation levels in local area; disposal of waste; how easily it could be decommissioned.

Pages 44–45 Renewable Sources of Energy
Multiple-choice questions
1. B   2. A   3. C   4. C   5. A
Short-answer questions
1. Renewable energy resources will not run out (will last forever, or at least for millennia); non-renewable energy sources are finite and will eventually run out (they cannot be replaced within a lifetime).
2. **Renewables – any three from:** hydroelectric power, biomass, tidal, wave, solar, geothermal, wind.
   Non-renewables – any three from: oil, gas, coal, nuclear
3. a) **Answers might include:** water reserves can diminish during droughts; land (habitats) have to be flooded to create reservoirs.
   b) **Answers might include:** tidal dams can destroy marine habitats; dams can stop fish migrating.
   c) **Answers might include:** power cannot be produced at night; poor weather conditions can limit power production.
   d) **Answers might include:** power can only be produced if there is sufficient wind to move the turbines; turbines can be frightening for livestock; some people consider turbines too noisy / ugly.
   e) **Answers might include:** volcanic action could damage the power station.
GCSE-style questions
1. a) They can give a lot of output power by allowing the water to run downhill; which drives turbines and generators placed there; the ease with which the water flow can be controlled enables a rapid response to demand.
   b) Stored GPE is converted to KE; KE is converted to electrical energy.
2. a) **Any two from:** effect on fish; effect of higher water levels on environment; spoils view.
   b) **Any two from:** cheaper electricity; job creation; 'clean' electricity.
3. ✎ Energy reaches the Earth from the Sun in the form of light and heat energy. The light from the Sun is captured by green plants and converted into useful energy by photosynthesis. This energy is then passed down the food chain when consumers eat the plants and eat each other. As fossil fuels, like coal and oil, are formed from the decayed remains

of plants and animals, the energy in these fuels originally came from the Sun. For many renewable energy resources, the Sun can also be seen as the original source of energy. Solar panels capture the Sun's energy directly. However, other renewable energy resources are dependent on the weather which is affected by the Sun. For example, wind turbines are reliant on wind, which is produced by convection currents caused by the Sun, and hydroelectrical power is dependent on rainfall, which is caused by the Sun evaporating water as part of the water cycle.

Pages 46–47 Electrical Energy and Power
Multiple-choice questions
1. B 2. A 3. C 4. B 5. A
Short-answer questions
1. $1000 \times 60 \text{ s} \times 60 \text{ min} = 3\,600\,000$ J
   (1 mark for calculation; 1 mark for answer)
2. $100 \times 60 \times 5 = 30\,000$ J
   (1 mark for calculation; 1 mark for answer)
3. a) amps (A)   b) Volts (V)   c) Watts (W)
4. **Answers may include:** Don't leave lights on; use energy-saving light bulbs; don't leave computers, etc. on standby (Accept any other sensible answers.)
GCSE-style questions
1. a) $0.1 \text{ kW} \times 12 \text{ hrs} \times 7 \text{ days} \times 10\text{p} = 84\text{p}$
   (1 mark for calculation; 1 mark for answer)
   b) i) 100 W bulb (10% useful energy):
   $100 \text{ W} \times \dfrac{10}{100\%} = 10$ W;
   18 W bulb (56% efficiency):
   $18 \text{ W} \times \dfrac{56}{100\%} = 10.08$ W;
   we get the same useful light output from the 18 W bulb but with less electrical power input.
   ii) $0.018 \times 12 \times 7 \times 10 = 15\text{p}$
   (1 mark for calculation; 1 mark for answer)
   iii) $84\text{p} - 15\text{p} = 69\text{p}$
   c) ✎ In terms of sustainability, the decision to ban 100 W bulbs is the right one. More efficient bulbs require less electricity, which means less fuel consumption. Since fossil fuels account for the majority of electricity production in the EU, this will help to conserve limited fossil fuel stocks. Emissions of pollutant gases and carbon dioxide, produced by burning fossil fuels, will also be reduced. However, to make a proper comparison, you would need to know how energy efficient the manufacturing process of both bulbs is. If a lot of energy is required to make the new bulb, it might outweigh the benefits.

Pages 48–49 Electricity Matters
Multiple-choice questions
1. C 2. D 3. D 4. B 5. C
Short-answer questions
1. a) electrical; generated; alternates; cables / power lines; step-down
   b) **Advantages may include:** power stations can be built close to fuel reserves; pollution can be kept away from densely populated areas; there is flexibility of power distribution; if a power station fails, coverage to all areas can still continue.
   Disadvantages may include: expensive to provide and maintain overhead / underground cabling; unsightly pylons and power cables; power is wasted during distribution
GCSE-style questions
1. a) The current keeps changing direction.
   b) i) Without the transformers power losses in the transmission lines would be too great; stepping up to high voltage for transmission reduces the current in the lines; and hence the power loss as heat.
   ii) Transformers work using electromagnetic induction; this requires a changing current; a direct current does not change.
2. a) $100\,000 \times 50 = 5\,000\,000$ W (= 5 MW)
   (1 mark for calculation; 1 mark for answer)
   b) $5\,000\,000 \text{ W} \times 0.9 = 4\,500\,000$ W (= 4.5 MW)
   (1 mark for calculation; 1 mark for answer)
   c) $\dfrac{4.5 \text{ MW}}{230 \text{ V}} = 19.6 \text{ kA}$ $\left(I = \dfrac{P}{V}\right)$
   (1 mark for calculation; 1 mark for answer)

3. ✎ I agree with the German government because although nuclear fuel is cheap and clean to use, in my opinion the safety issues by far outweigh these advantages. Nuclear fuel is cost effective because the fuel is not expensive and a small amount produces a large amount of energy. The energy transfer process does not produce carbon dioxide emissions like fossil fuels, so it does not contribute to the greenhouse effect and global warming. However, the radioactive waste that is produced remains dangerous to living things for thousands of years, so it has to be stored very carefully. In my view, this is not sustainable, as future generations will have to manage growing amounts of nuclear waste. There are also concerns about the safety of nuclear power stations in the events of a terrorist attack or a natural disaster like an earthquake. I do not think that it is worth taking these risks to save money. (Accept answers that disagree with decision, as long as supporting arguments are given.)

Pages 50–51 Particles and Heat Transfer
Multiple-choice questions
1. D 2. A 3. B 4. C 5. B
Short-answer questions
1. a) $0.2 \times 4200 \times 80 = 67\,200$ J **(1 mark for calculation; 1 mark for answer)**
   b) $25 \times 4200 \times 10 = 1\,050\,000$ J **(1 mark for calculation; 1 mark for answer)**
   c) Water has a large specific heat capacity; which means it can transfer a large amount of heat even for a relatively small temperature change.
GCSE-style questions
1. a) 100°C (the water was boiling)
   b) To ensure a fair test; so that the only variable affecting the results of the experiment is the colour of the box.
   c) i) matt black   ii) silver
   d) The major mechanism of heat transfer is radiation; conduction to the surrounding air and convection currents in the air are the same for all boxes; black surfaces are the most efficient radiators; whereas reflective surfaces are the least efficient.
   e) Ensure the results are repeatable.

Pages 52–53 Describing Waves
Multiple-choice questions
1. B 2. A 3. D 4. A 5. B
Short-answer questions
1. wavelength $= \dfrac{\text{wave speed}}{\text{frequency}} = \dfrac{20}{2} = 10$cm
   (1 mark for calculation; 1 mark for answer)
2. speed $= 0.34 \times 1000 = 340$ m/s;
   distance $= 340 \times 5 = 1700$ m
   (1 mark for calculation; 1 mark for answer)
3. A false B true C false
GCSE-style questions
1. a) vibrations / oscillations; energy; longitudinal; parallel
   b)
   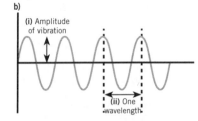
   (i) Amplitude of vibration
   (ii) One wavelength
   (Accept any other accurate indications of wavelength, e.g. trough to trough)
   c) i) The amplitude would be less.
   ii) The frequency would be higher / waves would be closer together.
   d) Sound is a longitudinal wave; the diagram illustrates a transverse wave; the air particle displacement in a sound wave is parallel to the x-axis (horizontal axis).
   e) compressions; rarefactions; further apart; amplitude

Pages 54–55 Wave Behaviour
Multiple-choice questions
1. B 2. C 3. A 4. D 5. B

Short-answer questions
1. a) The large angle of reflection should be circled.
   b) A new line should be drawn making the angle of incidence and angle of reflection equal.
   c) When a wave is reflected, the angle of reflection is equal to the angle of incidence.
GCSE-style questions
1. a) At the boundary between the air and the water of the pool, the light is refracted away from the normal; so the bottom of the pool appears closer to the surface than it really is. **(1 mark for suitable diagram)**
   b) Light under the water's surface does not have to pass from one material to another in order to reach the observer's eyes; therefore the light is not refracted and doesn't change the observer's perception of the bottom of the pool.
2. When waves pass through a gap that is a similar size to the wavelength they diffract (spread out); Light has an extremely small wavelength compared to buildings, so cannot diffract around corners; Sound has a longer wavelength and can diffract, as well as reflect, around buildings.
3. a) wavelength $= \dfrac{\text{wave speed}}{\text{frequency}} = \dfrac{1500}{30\,000}$
   $= 0.05\text{m} = 5\text{cm}$
   (1 mark for calculation; 1 mark for answer)
   b) $1500 \times 0.5 = 750$ m is the total distance travelled by the sound; therefore the distance to the submarine is 375 m.

Pages 56–57 Seismic Waves and the Earth
Multiple-choice questions
1. C 2. A 3. B 4. C 5. D
Short-answer questions
1. seismic; P; longitudinal; liquid; S; liquid; seismometers
2. convection
3. **Any two from:** jigsaw like match of shapes of continents; similar fossils on these continents, which are now thousands of miles apart; the magnetic alignment change in rock patterns many miles apart which reflect periodic variations in the Earth's magnetic field.
GCSE-style questions
1. a) i) and ii)

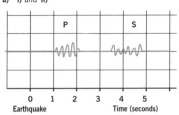

   b) $(3.5 - 1) \times 8 = 20$ km
   c) i) On the opposite side of the Earth.
   ii) B
   d) Scientists know that the Earth has a liquid core, because S-waves cannot travel directly though the Earth; By simulating earthquakes using controlled explosions they can trigger P-waves and S-waves; Monitoring these waves and analysing the data provides information about rock structure.

Pages 58–59 The Electromagnetic Spectrum
Multiple-choice questions
1. B 2. D 3. C 4. D 5. D
Short-answer questions
1. a) continuous; transverse; 300 000 000
   b) radio waves; microwaves; infrared; visible light; ultraviolet; X-rays; gamma rays.
2. The diagrams suggest that gamma rays have shorter wavelengths than X-rays; in fact, they overlap significantly in wavelength range.
GCSE-style questions
1. a) $3 \times \dfrac{10^8}{0.02} = 1.5 \times 10^{10}$ Hz
   (1 mark for calculation; 1 mark for answer)
   b) $3 \times \dfrac{10^8}{6} \times 10^{15} = 5 \times 10^{-8}$ m (= 50 nm)
   (1 mark for calculation; 1 mark for answer)
   c) i) 0.6 m; to 1 km
   ii) 250 m

2.
a) Intensity is the amount of energy per second arriving at a square meter of surface.

b) Moving closer to the source; increasing the output of the source.

c) Red light has the lowest frequency in the visible range; Therefore the photons have less energy and are insufficient to cause the film to react; It is not the total energy arriving per second that counts, but the energy per photon.

Pages 60–61 Light, Radio Waves and Microwaves
Multiple-choice questions
1. A 2. C 3. D 4. C 5. B

Short-answer questions
1. The electrons oscillate in response to the signal, forming an alternating electrical current.
2. **a)** To prevent the waves escaping and possibly harming people.

   b) Toast should be crisp, so it needs infrared radiation to heat and warm the surface; Microwaves would penetrate and cook from inside to a degree.
3. image; lens; retina.

GCSE-style questions
1. **a)** 🖉 In a microwave oven, the food is irradiated with microwaves. The food is rotated on a turntable to ensure even irradiation. The microwaves pass through glass and plastic packaging. The frequency of the microwaves used ensures that they are easily absorbed by water molecules in food. The absorbed microwaves increase the kinetic energy of the water molecules, which heats the food. Conduction and convection spread the heat throughout the food.

   b) There is water content in the Earth's atmosphere; microwaves of the wavelength range that is absorbed by water are therefore not suitable for transmission because they will be absorbed.

   c) Moisture in the atmosphere will absorb microwaves; so by measuring the amount of microwaves absorbed, the amount of water in the atmosphere can be calculated; An atmosphere with a high water content is more humid and likely to lead to rain or stormy weather.
2. **a)** high energy infrared; low energy ultraviolet.

   b) High energy ultraviolet; is absorbed in the upper levels of the atmosphere by ozone / infrared; is absorbed by the atmosphere.

Pages 62–63 Wireless Communications 1
Multiple-choice questions
1. D 2. C 3. B 4. A 5. B

Short-answer questions
1. Regeneration – The process of cleaning up a digital signal; Amplification – Increasing the size of a signal; Noise – Unwanted signals; Modulation – The changing of a signal that codes the information being sent.
2. **A** false **B** true **C** true **D** true
   E false **F** true

GCSE-style questions
1. Electromagnetic waves are diffracted by objects with dimensions of a similar size to one wavelength, causing them to spread out; radio waves, with wavelengths of a few metres or more, are diffracted by buildings, and natural features of the landscape; so reception does not have to be on a line of sight with the transmitter; microwaves, with wavelengths of a few centimetres, are not so readily diffracted; and so transmitters and receivers have to be in 'line of sight'.
2. **a)** **A** 3 **B** 1 **C** 5 **D** 2 **E** 4

   b) A code made up of just two values: 0 and 1.

   c) **i)** unwanted signals; that distort the original signal.

   ii) 🖉 The claim about unwanted noise is justified because digital signals give a better quality reception than analogue signals. This is because any noise picked up during transmission can be more easily removed. The original values can easily be restored because each pulse can only be a 0 or a 1. The process of cleaning up the signal is called regeneration. Analogue signals can be amplified, but any noise is amplified too.

Pages 64–65 Wireless Communications 2
Multiple-choice questions
1. B 2. A 3. B 4. A

Short-answer questions
1. **a)** **Any two from:** mobile phone; printer; Internet; local computer network (Accept any other sensible answer.)

   b) **Any three from:** ease of connectivity; portability of various devices; no wires needed; 24 hour access.
2. A3; B1; C2.

GCSE-style questions
1. **a)** Microwaves are used for heating / cooking food.

   b) The power involved for mobile phones is much less than that involved in a microwave oven; so the effects would be negligible.

   c) The effects of microwaves from mobile phones could be accumulative; or take a long time to become evident.

   d) **Any two from:** frequency and length of use of mobile phone; other occupational or lifestyle choices that might be relevant (e.g. smoking); difficulties in finding a matched group of people who are infrequent users of mobile phones **(Accept any other sensible answer.)**

   e) There is potential for bias if the scientists are being paid by a mobile phone company.

   f) Your answer should clearly state your opinion; assess the potential risk (the heating effect of microwaves); assess the vulnerability of those most at risk (young people); assess exposure (very low intensity, for prolonged periods of time); assess the heating effect at such levels; and assess the ethics of the proposal.

Pages 66–67 Infrared
Multiple-choice questions
1. A 2. C 3. C 4. B 5. A

Short-answer questions
1. If metal is heated to a high enough temperature it will emit light (red then white).
2. **A** false **B** false **C** true **D** true **E** true
3. glass; refractive index; total internal.

GCSE-style questions
1. **a)** Infrared

   b) **i)** Infrared has a higher frequency than radio waves and microwaves.

   ii) Infrared signals in fibre optic cables experience less interference; A stream of data can be transmitted very quickly; Digital signals can be multiplexed, so that lots of different signals can be sent along the fibre at the same time.
2. **a)** Nocturnal animals come out at night, so it would be difficult to capture them in the dark with a standard camera; The animal will be warmer than its surroundings so it will be visible in the infrared region at night.

   b) Infrared is outside the visible spectrum; so different visible colours (false colour) are used to depict different temperature ranges indicated by the infrared wavelength detected.

   c) A survivor trapped under rubble will be warmer than the surroundings; The warmth of their body will be visible in the infrared region; A thermal imager picks up on this temperature difference by observing the infrared region; **Any one limitation:** Use of the technique can be complicated in the presence of other sources of heat; It is also limited by the depth of material through which the infrared can be detected.

Pages 68–69 The Ionising Radiations
Multiple-choice questions
1. C 2. A 3. B 4. D

Short-answer questions
1. **Answers might include:** detecting forged bank notes; forensic detection of powders / fluids (Accept any other sensible answer.)
2. **a)** It knocks electrons out of the atoms electron shells, so the atom becomes charged (ionised).

   b) alpha; beta; gamma

   c) **i)** gamma **ii)** alpha

   d) alpha – a helium nucleus; beta – an electron.

GCSE-style questions
1. **a)** The risk to the radiographer would be too big as

they would be being exposed regularly; leading to a large cumulative exposure

   b) A patient has a single exposure, which carries a small risk; The risk is offset by the benefit to the patient from the information obtained; allowing diagnosis / better treatment of their medical problem.
2. **a)** Ionising radiation causes atoms to become charged, so they are more likely to take part in chemical reactions; If these atoms are inside the body's cells, this could damage or kill the cells; If the DNA of a cell is damaged it may mutate; Mutations can cause cells to grow out of control and become cancerous.

   b) The scientist should select a wide range of volunteers; to gain a picture of a cross-section of society.

   c) People within each group should be matched according to age, sex, ethnicity and lifestyle; relevant exposure to other known carcinogens (e.g. smoking); frequency and duration of sun bed use.

   d) A control group would be a group of people who do not use sun beds; this provides a good comparison so that other factors can be ruled out.

   e) A correlation shows a pattern / relationship; but it is not proof of cause.

Pages 70–71 The Atmosphere
Multiple-choice questions
1. D 2. D 3. B 4. A 5. A

Short-answer questions
1. **a)** Low energy infrared

   b) Light and high energy infrared
2. **A** false **B** false **C** true **D** true
   E false **F** true

GCSE-style questions
1. **a)** **Any two from:** extreme weather conditions; rising sea levels; expansion of oceans / flooding of lowlands; some regions no longer able to grow food crops (Accept any other sensible answer.)

   b) Greenhouse gases behave like the glass in a greenhouse; They allow high energy infrared from the sun into the atmosphere, but prevent low energy infrared from escaping, i.e. they trap heat.

   c) **Any two from:** increased combustion of fossil fuels in cars / vehicles; increased burning of fossil fuels to provide electricity; deforestation (less carbon dioxide being removed from the atmosphere by photosynthesis) (Accept any other sensible answer.)

   d) **Any one from:** There have been other periods of extreme weather (i.e. ice ages and droughts) in the history of the Earth; it is difficult to specify what temperature increase / duration constitutes global warming; there are political issues involved (Accept any other sensible answer.)
2. **a)** The ozone layer is a layer of ozone gas in the upper atmosphere; It absorbs some UV, limiting the amount that reaches Earth.

   b) Greater UV exposure will lead to greater incidence of sunburn, skin cancer and cataracts.

   c) The concentration of CFCs in the atmosphere increased; this reacted with the ozone gases, damaging the ozone layer.

Pages 72–73 The Solar System and Scale
Multiple-choice questions
1. C 2. C 3. B 4. B 5. B

Short-answer questions
1. B; A; D; E; C.
2. Sun – The star at the centre of the Solar System; Moon – A natural satellite in orbit around a planet; Asteroid – A rock, up to about 1 km in diameter, in orbit around the Sun; Comet – Accumulated ice and dust, with a nucleus that vaporises when it comes close to the Sun; Meteor – A small rock, usually from a comet, entering the Earth's atmosphere.

1. a)

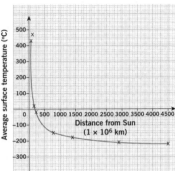

(1 mark for scale and label on *y*-axis; 1 mark for scale and label on *x*-axis; 1 mark for accurately plotted points; 1 mark for line of best fit.)

b) The further a planet is from the Sun, the colder its average surface temperature; this is because radiation from the Sun is less intense at greater distances.

c) Venus

d) The atmosphere on Venus may have a greenhouse effect. (Accept any other sensible answer.)

Pages 74–75 Galaxies and Red-Shift
Multiple-choice questions
1. B   **2.** C   **3.** B   **4.** D   **5.** C
Short-answer questions
1. a) The further away the galaxy is, the faster it moves away.
b) The measured red-shift can be used to determine distance
2. expanding; Big Bang; further; greater; faster; away; Doppler effect; blue.
GCSE-style questions
1. a) Answers may include: Insufficient data may be available to distinguish between alternatives; personal opinion may influence a scientist's choice between options (Accept any other sensible answer.)
b) Any three from: presentation at scientific conferences; publication in scientific journals; peer review; reproduction of results by other scientists.
c) A, B and E
2. ✏ Light from distant stars can be analysed with a spectrometer. Each element produces a unique set of spectral lines (absorption spectrum), so the lines can be used to identify which elements are present. Dark lines represent wavelengths that have been absorbed by elements in the outer regions of the star. Bright lines are wavelengths emitted by atoms of hot gases. The elements present in the outer regions of the star will each absorb specific wavelengths, so the absorption spectrum produced. If the star is moving away from the Earth the absorption spectrum is shifted towards longer wavelengths (red shift). The extent of the shift is indicative of the speed.

Pages 76–77 Expanding Universe and Big Bang
Multiple-choice questions
1. B   **2.** D   **3.** C   **4.** D   **5.** A
Short-answer questions
1. The distances to spiral nebulae are greater than the size of the Milky Way. – Spiral nebulae are outside the Milky Way and are likely to be distant galaxies; The light from all the distant galaxies is red-shifted. – All the distant galaxies are moving away from us; The further away the galaxy is, the bigger the red-shift – The further away a galaxy is, the faster it is moving.
2. theory; hypothesis; radiation; hypothesis; confidence; theory.
GCSE-style questions
1. a) $0.05 \times (3 \times 10^8) = 1.5 \times 10^7$ m/s
(1 mark for calculation; 1 mark for answer)
b) $0.05 \times 5 = 0.25 = 25$ cm
(1 mark for calculation; 1 mark for answer)
c) i) A

ii) $500 \times 10^6 \times (3 \times 10^8) \times 365$ days $\times 24$ hours $\times 60$ minutes $\times$ 60 seconds $= 4.7 \times 10^{24}$ m **(1 mark for calculation; 1 mark for answer)**

d) The Universe is everything that exists (there is nothing outside the Universe); The age of the Universe can be estimated by using red-shift data to look at the distance of objects from Earth and the speed at which they are moving away from Earth; this information can be used to estimate the time since all distant objects first separated and started moving apart (i.e. when the Big Bang took place).

CHEMISTRY

Pages 78–79 Atoms and Elements
Multiple-choice questions
1. B   **2.** C   **3.** B   **4.** B   **5.** D
Short-answer questions
1. electrons; neutrons; protons; 1; electrons; neutrons; protons; electrons
2. a) i) 184   **ii)** 74
b) One atom of tungsten has 74 protons; 110 neutrons; and 74 electrons.
GCSE-style questions
1.

	Relative mass	Relative charge	Where found in the atom
Electron	$\dfrac{1}{1840}$	−1	shells
Proton	1	+1	nucleus
Neutron	1	0	nucleus

2. a) i) proton   **ii)** neutron   **iii)** electron
b) the orbits around a nucleus; in which the electrons are found
c) mass number = protons + neutrons = 3 + 4 = 7 atomic number = number of protons = 3
d) $^{7}_{3}\text{Li}$

Pages 80–81 Formulae and Equations
Multiple-choice questions
1. B   **2.** C   **3.** D   **4.** C   **5** D
Short-answer questions
1. nitrogen, hydrogen, oxygen; ratio 1:5:1
2. a compound; because there are two capital letters, so two different elements
3. allow 1 mark for hydrogen and oxygen, but two marks for water: H_2O
4. Two; magnesium atoms; in a solid state; react with one; molecule of oxygen (containing two oxygen atoms); in a gaseous state; to form the compound magnesium oxide; in a solid state; The magnesium and oxygen atoms are combined in the ratio 1:1.
GCSE-style questions
1. a) all are compounds; containing just two elements
b) i) NaCl   **ii)** CuO
c) CO_2 and SO_2; because both have two oxygen atoms
d) Any two from: tells the scientist which elements are present; tells the scientist the ratio of atoms of each element; the formula is the same in all languages
e) nitrogen and hydrogen have combined; in the ratio 1:3

Pages 82–83 Balancing Equations and Gas Tests
Multiple-choice questions
1. B   **2.** B   **3.** A   **4.** A   **5.** D
Short-answer questions
1. a) 2 – 2
b) – – 2
c) – 2 – 2
d) – 3 2
e) – 2 – 2
f) 3 2 3 3
(1 mark for each correct row)
GCSE-style questions
1. 1. products
2. atoms; sides
3. number; one
4. state

2. a) i) 6 carbon, 12 hydrogen, 18 oxygen
ii) 6 carbon, 12 hydrogen, 18 oxygen
b) The equation balances; there are the same number of each kind of atom on both sides of the equation
c) Bubble the gas through limewater using a delivery tube; if carbon dioxide is present the limewater will turn cloudy.

Pages 84–85 Ionic and Covalent Bonding
Multiple-choice questions
1. B   **2.** D   **3.** A   **4.** C   **5.** B
Short-answer questions
a) i) 1   **ii)** 6   **iii)** 4   **iv)** 4
b)

(1 mark each for transfer of electron from lithium to fluorine shown; correct electronic structure of ions; charges on ions)
GCSE-style questions
1. a) hydrogen; carbon; nitrogen
b) i) 1   **ii)** 4   **iii)** 3)
c) triple
2. a) metal, it forms ionic bonds
b) i) 2+   **ii)** YO
c)

(1 mark for (•×) in overlap; 2 marks for each atom having 8 electrons)

Pages 86–87 Plate Tectonics
Multiple-choice questions
1. D   **2.** C   **3.** A   **4.** B   **5.** A
Short-answer questions
1. **A** crust   **B** core   **C** mantle
2. convection currents; in the mantle
3. magma is below ground; lava is above ground
4. oceanic crust is mainly composed of basalt; continental crust is composed of sedimentary, igneous and metamorphic rock.
GCSE-style questions
1. a) the shapes of the major continents seem to fit together; as though they had once been joined together
b) fossils of the same creatures were found on opposite sides of the oceans; indicating that land masses had once been joined together
c) it contradicted religious beliefs; continents cannot be seen moving; Wegener could not explain how or why the continents moved
d) movement of the continents is very slow and measuring instruments were not sensitive enough in those days
e) Britain has moved through tropical climate zones as it has drifted; and fossils were laid down at that time

Pages 88–89 Evolution of the Atmosphere
Multiple-choice questions
1. A   **2.** C   **3.** A   **4.** B   **5.** B
Short-answer questions
1. 78% nitrogen; 21% oxygen
2. photosynthesis; by green plants
3. water vapour in the atmosphere; condensed as Earth cooled
4. CH_4; and NH_3
5. O_3; It is in the upper atmosphere
GCSE-style questions
1. a) they removed carbon dioxide from the atmosphere; to make their shells
b) it has been turned into stable compounds; such as carbonates
c) denitrifying; bacteria
d) they have reduced carbon dioxide; and increased oxygen
e) carbon dioxide dissolves in seawater; to make carbonic acid

Pages 90–91 Atmospheric Gases
Multiple-choice questions
1. D   2. B   3. B   4. C   5. D
Short-answer questions
1. 0; 7; 8; 2
2. Helium is used in balloons / airships; it allows them to float as it is less dense than air.
GCSE-style questions
1. a) CO_2 b) D   c) respiration; decay.
   d) Plants take in carbon dioxide dioxide during photosynthesis; and release oxygen.
   e) This practice could lead to an increase in carbon dioxide in the atmosphere; because less trees are available to remove the gas by photosynthesis; burning trees as fuel releases carbon dioxide into the atmosphere; and the livestock being introduced to the land will release carbon dioxide through respiration.

Pages 92–93 Pollution of the Atmosphere
Multiple-choice questions
1. B   2. B   3. C   4. C   5. B
Short-answer questions
1. $S + O_2 \longrightarrow SO_2$ (1 mark for products; 1 mark for balanced equation)
2. **Any two from:** acid rain; global warming/greenhouse effect; photochemical smog
3. to obtain maximum heat energy; to produce no toxic carbon monoxide/soot
4. carbon dioxide; nitrogen
5. so that more catalyst is in contact with the gases; to increase the rate of conversion
GCSE-style questions
1. a) $CH_4 + 2O_2 \longrightarrow CO_2 + 2H_2O$
      (1 mark for products; 1 mark for balanced equation)
   b) carbon monoxide is produced; which is very toxic
   c) water vapour is one product; which condenses when it meets cold air
   d) **Any three from:** check sufficient air can enter; check no carbon monoxide produced; check flue is not blocked; check no gas is leaking
   e) **Any one from:** so they do not have to remember when to get the boiler serviced; check for any problems; easily get engineer if something goes wrong

Pages 94–95 Fuels
Multiple-choice questions
1. A   2. B   3. C   4 C   5. D
Short-answer questions
1. they are being used at a greater rate; than they are naturally being formed/take millions of years to form
2. mixture; hydrocarbons; carbon; fractions.
3. they ignite better; and are more likely to undergo complete combustion
4. the hydrocarbons with the lowest boiling points; and the shortest carbon chains
GCSE-style questions
1. a) petroleum gas; kerosene
   b) Vapours enter the column and travel upwards; from level to level until they reach the temperature at which they condense; Different fractions condense at different levels.
   c) they can be cracked; to make more valuable hydrocarbons
   d) i) fuel for aircraft   ii) making roads / roofs

Pages 96–97 Organic Chemistry
Multiple-choice questions
1. B   2. D   3. A   4. C   5. A
Short-answer questions
1. a) Propane
   b)
   H H
   H-C-C-H
   H H
   c) normal butane
   C_4H_{10}

   H H H H
   H-C-C-C-C-H
   H H H H

   d) iso-butane
   C_4H_{10}

   H H H
   H-C-C-C-H
   H C H
   H-C-H
   H

   (1 mark for each correct name or formula)
GCSE-style questions
1. a) cracking
   b) i) methane or CH_4 ii) ethene or C_2H_4
   c) alkenes decolourise bromine water; alkanes do not react
2. a) i) C_2H_6 ii) C_5H_{12}
   b) any value greater than $30\,^{\circ}C$
   c) water vapour from gas burning; condenses on cold metal
   d) butane has a higher melting point than propane; and would turn into a liquid

Pages 98–99 Ethanol
Multiple-choice questions
1. C   2. B   3. D   4. C   5. B
Short-answer questions
1. a) sugar (sugar beet / sugar cane)
   b) i) because the raw materials from which it is produced can be easily replaced (by growing more plants).
      ii) ethanol burns very cleanly
      iii) **Any one of:** it produces less energy than petrol; large areas of land are required to grow the plants.
GCSE-style questions
1. a) i) **Any two from:** sugar; yeast; water
      ii) limewater
   b) $25–50\,^{\circ}C$
   c) $2CO_2$
   d) no more bubbles of carbon dioxide
   e) limewater and bung; stop air getting in
   f) i) plant matter and animal waste (used as fuel)
      ii) ✏ Ethanol can be made from biomass. A genetically modified *E. coli* bacterium which produces enzymes is added to the biomass. These enzymes, under the right conditions, ferment the sugars in the biomass. The optimum conditions are a pH of between 6.0 and 7.0, a good supply of oxygen and a temperature of about $30\,^{\circ}C$.

Pages 100–101 Plastics
Multiple-choice questions
1. B   2. D   3. A   4. D   5. D
Short-answer questions
1. **Any two from:** cotton; wood; leather; silk; wool (or other sensible answer)
2. **Any one from:** polyethene from ethene; polypropene from propene; PVC from vinyl chloride; PTFE (Teflon) from tetrafluoroethene
3. PVC is lightweight; and it will not corrode
4. crystallinity increases rigidity; and it makes the plastic more brittle
5. it has very low friction; and food will not stick to it
GCSE-style questions
1. a) ethene molecules are made to join together; at high pressure with a catalyst
   b) they must be melted
   c) polythene is thermoplastic; as it has to be heated to soften it
   d) **Any two from:** the bucket is cheaper; lighter; will not corrode
   e) the plasticiser makes the bucket more flexible; and less likely to crack; if dropped or overloaded

Pages 102–103 Vegetable Oils
Multiple-choice questions
1. B   2. B   3. A   4. D   5. B
Short-answer questions
1. **Any two from:** corn; rapeseed; olives; soya; coconut (or other sensible answer)
2. unsaturated molecules in vegetable oils have kinks; that stop them packing so close together
3. from orange-brown; to colourless
4. the molecules have to lose some of the C=C bonds; so that they can solidify at room temperature

5. it helps an insoluble oil or fat; mix fully with water, forming an emulsion
GCSE-style questions
1. a) molecules which have more than one; C=C bond
   b) it has been hydrogenated; by reacting it with hydrogen
   c) there are fewer C=C double bonds in margarine than there were in the unprocessed vegetable oil
   d) people are used to spreading a solid onto their bread; and they may prefer the taste
   e) saturated fat in the diet increases blood cholesterol; which is linked to heart disease

Pages 104–105 Iron and Steel
Multiple-choice questions
1. D   2. B   3. A   4. B   5. D
Short-answer questions
1. a) R is limestone; S is air
   b) Steel is harder than wrought iron; and more versatile.
GCSE-style questions
1. a) i) to stop air getting in
      ii) to stop air getting into the water
      iii) to remove dissolved air from the water
      iv) to remove water vapour
   b)

	A	B
A	yes	
B		no
C	no	yes
D	yes	yes

   (1 mark for each correct row)

Pages 106–107 Transition Metals
Multiple-choice questions
1. B   2. D   3. B   4. A   5. C
Short-answer questions
1. a) i) T
      ii) high density, coloured compounds
   b) R – Mg;   S – Na;   T – Cu
GCSE-style questions
1. a) i) titanium dioxide + chlorine + carbon $\longrightarrow$ titanium(IV) chloride + carbon monoxide
      ii) non-conductor of electricity; solid
      iii)

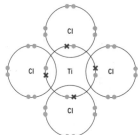

      (1 mark each for 4 covalent bonds; rest of molecule)
      iv) a type of distillation that separates two substances with boiling points that are very close to each other (OWTTE)
   b) i) it stops magnesium reacting with air
      ii) $2Mg(s) + TiCl_4(l) \longrightarrow Ti(s) + 2MgCl_2(s)$
         (1 mark for products; 1 mark for for balanced equation; 1 mark for state symbols)
      iii) electrolysis of molten magnesium chloride
   c) variable valency; coloured compounds

Pages 108–109 Copper
Multiple-choice questions
1. D   2. B   3. C   4. D   5. B
Short-answer questions
1. a) copper(II) ion; sulfate ion; hydrogen ion; hydroxide ion
   b) it is positive
   c) it stays the same colour; copper ions are formed at the anode; at the same rate as copper ions are deposited at the cathode
   d) i) oxygen
      ii) copper
GCSE-style questions
1. a) i) chalcopyrite + oxygen $\longrightarrow$ copper(I) sulfide + iron(II) oxide + sulfur dioxide
         (1 mark for reactants; 1 mark for products; 1 mark for balanced equation)
      ii) iron is more reactive than copper
   b) i) manufacture of iron

ii) $Cu_2S(s) + O_2(g) \longrightarrow 2Cu(s) + SO_2(g)$
   (1 mark for products; 1 mark for balanced equation)
c) copper(II) oxide; CuO; black
d) variable valency; coloured compounds
e) carbon dioxide; water vapour

Pages 110–111 Aluminium
Multiple-choice questions
1. A 2. A 3. B 4. A 5. A
Short-answer questions
1. metal; bauxite; carbon; electrolysis; oxide; cans
GCSE-style questions
1. a) X is anode; Y is carbon; Z is aluminium
   b) using electricity to break down or decompose; a compound
   c) Al^{3+}; O^{2-}; Na^+
   d) reduction is the removal of oxygen; aluminium oxide has been reduced to aluminium
   e) i) cheaper electricity
      ii) stops heat energy escaping

Pages 112–113 Limestone
Multiple-choice questions
1. C 2. C 3. D 4. A 5. D
Short-answer questions
1. a) sand (silicon dioxide); soda (sodium carbonate)
   b) clay c) cement d) sedimentary e) ions
2. **Any three from:** cotton; paper; wool; silk; leather; wood
GCSE-style questions
1. a) 1; 3
   b) i) calcium oxide
      ii) thermal; decomposition
   c) i) to stop dust getting into the atmosphere
      ii) nitrogen is in air; it is an unreactive gas and passes through the furnace
   d) high melting point
   e) i) calcium hydroxide
      ii) $Ca(OH)_2$
      iii) soils that are too acidic; will be neutralised by the quicklime
   f) i) $Sr(OH)_2$
      ii) $SrSO_4$

Pages 114–115 Salts and Metal Carbonates
Multiple-choice questions
1. B 2. A 3. C 4. D 5. B
Short-answer questions
1. $HCl + NaOH \longrightarrow NaCl + H_2O$
   (1 mark for products; 1 mark for balanced equation)
2. calcium nitrate; and water
3. hydrogen gas; which burns with a squeaky pop when a lighted splint is applied
4. green; to black
5. zinc sulfate; $ZnSO_4$
GCSE-style questions
1. a) i) carbon dioxide
      ii) exothermic
      iii) to speed up the rate of reaction/provide a large surface area
   b) i) no carbon dioxide given off/no bubbles
      ii) green solid left, which does not react any more
   c) to remove excess copper(II) carbonate
   d) i) the liquid that has passed through the filter paper
      ii) a solution that contains as much dissolved substance as possibleat a particular temperature
   e) water vapour
   f) i) copper(II) carbonate + sulfuric acid $\longrightarrow$ copper(II) sulfate + carbon dioxide + water
      ii) $CuCO_3(s) + H_2SO_4(aq) \longrightarrow$ $CuSO_4(aq) + CO_2(g) + H_2O(l)$
      (1 mark for reactants; 1 mark for products)

Pages 116–117 The Electrolysis of Sodium Chloride Solution
Multiple-choice questions
1. B 2. D 3. C 4. D 5. C
Short-answer questions
1. it lowers the melting point of ice; causing ice to melt
2. it produces three useful products: chlorine; hydrogen; and sodium hydroxide.

3. to prevent them from reacting with the useful products made.
4. reduction
5. oxidation
GCSE-style questions
1. a) hydrogen; chlorine
   b) they lose electrons to become atoms; which join together to make Cl_2 molecules
   c) sodium hydroxide is produced; sodium hydroxide solution is alkaline
   d) $2H^+ + 2e^- \longrightarrow H_2$
      (1 mark for products; 1 mark for balanced equation)
   e) **Any two from:** bleach; PVC; water sterilisers; hydrochloric acid; HCFCs

Answer all parts of all questions. Continue on a separate sheet of paper if necessary.

1 Microwaves are absorbed by water. The frequency of the microwaves determines how well they are absorbed.

a) ✎ With reference to the statement above, explain how microwaves are used to cook food in microwave ovens. **(6 marks)**

....

....

....

....

....

....

b) Explain why the property of microwaves described above means that only certain frequencies of microwave can be used for wireless communications. **(2 marks)**

....

....

....

c) Using your knowledge of the properties of microwaves, explain how microwaves might be used to help with weather forecasting. **(3 marks)**

....

....

....

2 Electromagnetic radiation from the Sun that reaches the Earth covers a broader spectrum than the visible region that we see.

a) Apart from visible light, state two types of radiation from the Sun that penetrate to the Earth's surface. **(2 marks)**

....

b) State one type of radiation from the Sun that fails to reach the surface and explain why. **(2 marks)**

....

....

Physics

Score   / 15

How well did you do?

| 0–6 | Try again | 7–12 | Getting there | 13–19 | Good work | 20–27 | Excellent! |

For more information on this topic, see pages 62–63 of your Success Revision Guide.

Wireless Communications 1

Multiple-choice questions

Choose just one answer: A, B, C or D.

1 Which waves have to be used in direct 'line of sight' telecommunication? **(1 mark)**
A analogue
B digital
C radio waves
D microwaves

2 Which waves can pass through the Earth's atmosphere and diffract around large obstacles? **(1 mark)**
A analogue
B digital
C radio waves
D microwaves

3 Which signals are coded by 1s and Os? **(1 mark)**
A analogue
B digital

C radio waves
D microwaves

4 Which signals can have a continuous range of values? **(1 mark)**
A analogue
B digital
C radio waves
D microwaves

5 Which signals give the best quality of reception and sound reproduction? **(1 mark)**
A analogue
B digital
C radio waves
D microwaves

Score / 5

Short-answer questions

1 Draw one line from each word to the correct definition. (3 marks)

Regeneration	The changing of a signal that codes the information being sent
Amplification	The process of cleaning up a digital signal
Noise	Unwanted signals
Modulation	Increasing the size of a signal

2 True or false?   True   False   (6 marks)

A We can hear radio waves but we cannot hear microwaves.   ☐   ☐

B Microwaves pass through the Earth's atmosphere.   ☐   ☐

C Radio waves have a lower frequency than microwaves.   ☐   ☐

D Radio waves diffract more than microwaves.   ☐   ☐

E Light travels faster than radio waves.   ☐   ☐

F Radio waves and microwaves can be used as carrier waves.   ☐   ☐

Score / 9

Answer all parts of all questions. Continue on a separate sheet of paper if necessary.

1 Microwaves and radio waves are both used extensively for telecommunication.

Microwave transmitters and receivers must be correctly aligned, whereas this is not the case for radio or television reception.

With reference to their wavelengths, explain this behaviour of radio waves and microwaves. **(5 marks)**

....

....

....

....

....

....

2 Digital television broadcasting is replacing the old analogue system.

a) Number the statements **A–E** below to describe how information is transmitted using digital technology. **(5 marks)**

A The codes are added to a carrier wave. ....

B The information is divided into tiny segments of time. ....

C The signal is received and decoded to recover the original information. ....

D Each segment is given a numerical value using binary code. ....

E The wave is transmitted. ....

b) State what a binary code is. **(1 mark)**

....

c) An advertisement for the national switchover to digital transmission claims 'unwanted noise on your television screen is a thing of the past with digital television'.

i) Describe what is meant by the term 'noise' in this context. **(2 marks)**

....

....

ii) ✎ Explain whether or not the claim being made in the advertisement is justified. **(6 marks)**
(Answer on a separate piece of paper.)

Score / 19

Physics

How well did you do?

| 0–10 | Try again | 11–18 | Getting there | 19–25 | Good work | 26–33 | Excellent! |

For more information on this topic, see pages 64–65 of your Success Revision Guide.

Wireless Communications 2

Multiple-choice questions

Choose just one answer: A, B, C or D.

1 Which electromagnetic waves are used for satellite communications? **(1 mark)**
- **A** radio waves
- **B** microwaves
- **C** light waves
- **D** heat waves

2 Which electromagnetic waves are used for television broadcasts? **(1 mark)**
- **A** radio waves
- **B** light waves
- **C** microwaves
- **D** sound waves

3 Which of the following is NOT an advantage of a wireless phone connection? **(1 mark)**
- **A** no wires are needed
- **B** the user needs to be close to a transmitter mast
- **C** increased portability
- **D** phone and internet connectivity are constantly available

4 When carrying out investigations into the health effects of mobile phone use, why do scientists match their samples so that they are comparing the same type of people? **(1 mark)**
- **A** to minimise the number of external factors that could affect the results
- **B** to minimise the cost of the investigation
- **C** because they are only interested in the effects on certain groups of people
- **D** because it makes it easier to find people to study

Score / 4

Short-answer questions

1 Computer and communication technology is increasingly 'wireless'.

a) State two pieces of equipment that a personal computer might routinely be connected to. **(2 marks)**

....

b) State three advantages of using wireless communication in the workplace or at home. **(3 marks)**

....

....

2 Match the graphs A to C with the most appropriate description of how the variables relate. **(2 marks)**

1. negative correlation between X and Y
2. no correlation between X and Y
3. positive correlation between X and Y

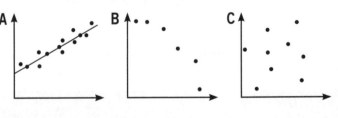

....

Score / 7

Answer all parts of all questions. Continue on a separate sheet of paper if necessary.

1 The 'explosion' in recent years of the use of microwave technology for mobile phones has caused some people to be alarmed at the possible health implications.

One concern is that because the handset is held close to the head, the microwaves have a heating effect on the brain.

a) State which other use of microwaves would seem to support the possibility of such a risk. **(1 mark)**

b) It is generally thought that the risk to health caused by the heating effect of microwaves from mobile phones is negligible. With reference to your answer to part **a)**, explain why this is. **(2 marks)**

c) The only reliable way to determine if there is a significant health risk is to carry out a long-term study. Describe why it is necessary for the study to run for many years. **(2 marks)**

d) State two other factors that would need to be considered when setting up such a study to ensure reliable results. **(2 marks)**

e) Describe why is it important that the scientists who carry out such investigations are independent of the mobile phone companies. **(1 mark)**

f) ✐ A mobile phone company offers to pay a school money to install a transmitter mast on the top of a school building. Many of the parents and teachers are planning a protest.

Suggest whether you think the proposal is a good idea or not and explain your answer. **(6 marks)**

Score   / 14

How well did you do?

| 0–6 | Try again | 7–13 | Getting there | 14–19 | Good work | 20–25 | Excellent! |

For more information on this topic, see pages 66–67 of your Success Revision Guide.

Infrared

Multiple-choice questions

Choose just one answer: A, B, C or D.

1 Optical fibres can carry signals to and from many homes and businesses at the same time, because of a process called: **(1 mark)**
- **A** multiplexing
- **B** time sharing
- **C** divergence
- **D** total internal reflection

2 Which of the following applications does not use infrared? **(1 mark)**
- **A** security sensors
- **B** remote control devices
- **C** wireless Internet access
- **D** thermal imaging

3 The process by which light is transmitted using optical fibre requires the angle of incidence to be: **(1 mark)**
- **A** less than 90°
- **B** 0°
- **C** greater than the critical angle
- **D** less than the critical angle

4 What is the name of the process by which infrared radiation and light are transmitted down optical fibres? **(1 mark)**
- **A** total external reflection
- **B** total internal reflection
- **C** diffraction
- **D** refraction

5 A device that produces a narrow beam of intense radiation of one colour is called a: **(1 mark)**
- **A** laser
- **B** Sun lamp
- **C** LED
- **D** bulb

Score   / 5

Short-answer questions

1 Describe how it is possible to make a piece of metal emit visible light. (1 mark)

....

2 True or false?

	True	False	(5 marks)
A Light is a longitudinal wave.	☐	☐	
B Red light has a higher frequency than blue light.	☐	☐	
C X-ray photons have more energy than ultraviolet photons.	☐	☐	
D Radio waves diffract more easily than microwaves.	☐	☐	
E Lasers are used to read the information stored on a compact disc.	☐	☐	

3 Fill in the missing words to complete the following passage.

Digital signals can be efficiently transmitted as infrared along optical fibres made of two layers of

.... Each layer has a different .... Every time the light

beam hits the boundary between the two layers .... reflection directs

it back into the fibre.

(3 marks)

Score   / 9

Answer all parts of all questions. Continue on a separate sheet of paper if necessary.

1 Originally Broadband Internet was delivered along telephone lines, but the use of new fibre optic cables is becoming increasingly popular.

a) State which type of electromagnetic waves are used to transmit signals down fibre optic cables. **(1 mark)**

b) i) Describe how the frequency of this type of wave compares to radio waves and microwaves. **(1 mark)**

ii) Explain the advantages of using fibre optic cables to transmit Broadband. **(3 marks)**

2 A naturalist wishing to study the behaviour of a nocturnal mammal invests in a camera with night vision technology, which is capable of detecting infrared.

a) Explain why such technology will be useful to monitor the activity of nocturnal animals. **(2 marks)**

b) The camera manual states that 'The detected infrared is converted and shown in false colour'. Describe what this means. **(2 marks)**

c) Similar technology is employed by rescue services, for example, to seek out survivors buried under rubble, following an earthquake. In this context, the use of infrared it is often referred to as 'thermal imaging'. Explain what this means and what limitations the technique has. **(4 marks)**

Score   / 13

Physics

How well did you do?

| 0–6 | Try again | 7–13 | Getting there | 14–20 | Good work | 21–27 | Excellent! |

For more information on this topic, see pages 68–69 of your Success Revision Guide.

The Ionising Radiations

Multiple-choice questions

Choose just one answer: A, B, C or D.

1 Which electromagnetic waves come from radioactive sources? **(1 mark)**
- **A** UV
- **B** X-ray
- **C** gamma
- **D** light

2 Which of the following electromagnetic waves are the most highly penetrating? **(1 mark)**
- **A** gamma
- **B** light
- **C** UV
- **D** radio

3 Which electromagnetic waves can cause sun burn? **(1 mark)**
- **A** light
- **B** UV
- **C** X-ray
- **D** gamma

4 Which waves pose the least risk of cell damage due to ionisation? **(1 mark)**
- **A** gamma
- **B** X-ray
- **C** UV
- **D** light

Score   / 4

Short-answer questions

1 Describe one way in which UV light can be used to prevent / detect criminal activity.   (1 mark)

2 a) Describe how radiation can ionise atoms.   (1 mark)

b) State the three types of ionising radiation released by radioactive materials.   (3 marks)

c) i) State which type of ionising radiation is the most penetrating.   (1 mark)

ii) State which type of ionising radiation is the least penetrating.   (1 mark)

d) State which two types of ionising radiation are particles and describe what they consist of.   (2 marks)

Score   / 9

Physics

68

Answer all parts of all questions. Continue on a separate sheet of paper if necessary.

1 X-rays are useful in diagnosing broken bones.

a) Explain why the radiographer leaves the room while the X-ray of a patient is taken. **(2 marks)**

b) Using the idea of risk versus benefit, explain why it is acceptable to expose the patient to X-rays. **(3 marks)**

2 A scientist is asked to carry out an investigation into whether there is a positive correlation between the level of sun bed use and an individual's chances of developing skin cancer.

a) Explain why exposure to ionising radiation is likely to increase the risk of cancer. **(4 marks)**

b) Describe what type of sample of people the scientist should aim to use for this investigation. **(2 marks)**

c) Explain how the scientist should group the people in his sample. **(3 marks)**

d) The scientists decide to us a control group. Explain what this means. **(2 marks)**

e) Explain why an investigation into correlation can never be totally conclusive. **(2 marks)**

Score   / 18

Physics

How well did you do?

| 0–8 | Try again | 9–16 | Getting there | 17–24 | Good work | 25–31 | Excellent! |

For more information on this topic, see pages 70–71 of your Success Revision Guide.

The Atmosphere

Multiple-choice questions

Choose just one answer: A, B, C or D.

1 Infrared frequencies, emitted by the Earth, are absorbed by gases in the atmosphere. Which of the following is NOT one of those gases? **(1 mark)**
   A methane
   B carbon dioxide
   C water vapour
   D ozone

2 Which of the following does NOT contribute to the greenhouse effect? **(1 mark)**
   A burning fossil fuels
   B cattle farming
   C deforestation
   D rising sea levels

3 Which of these is produced when burning fossil fuels? **(1 mark)**

   A oxygen
   B carbon dioxide
   C hydrogen
   D ozone

4 The ozone layer is responsible for: **(1 mark)**
   A absorbing dangerous UV radiation
   B filtering the air we breathe
   C filtering out infrared radiation
   D absorbing carbon dioxide

5 Depletion of which of these gases in the atmosphere is likely to lead to more cases of skin cancer? **(1 mark)**
   A ozone
   B carbon dioxide
   C water vapour
   D methane

Score   / 5

Short-answer questions

1 The 'greenhouse effect' is so called because it mirrors the way in which a greenhouse works.

   a) State which type of electromagnetic radiation is absorbed by the glass in a greenhouse. (1 mark)

   ....

   b) State which type of electromagnetic radiation passes though the glass. (1 mark)

   ....

2 True or false?   True   False   (6 marks)

   A Infrared radiation can cause skin cancer.   ☐   ☐

   B Low frequency ultraviolet radiation cannot penetrate the atmosphere. ☐   ☐

   C CFCs are thought to affect the ozone layer in the Earth's atmosphere. ☐   ☐

   D Infrared photons are less energetic than ultraviolet photons. ☐   ☐

   E If the distance to a source of light is double the intensity
       received halves.   ☐   ☐

   F The intensity of sunlight is at its daily maximum around noon. ☐   ☐

Score   / 8

Answer all parts of all questions. Continue on a separate sheet of paper if necessary.

1 Global warming is a major environmental concern. One of the main contributing factors is thought to be the increase in emissions of 'greenhouse gases' over the past 200 years.

a) State two consequences of global warming. **(2 marks)**

b) Explain what is meant by the term 'greenhouse gases'. **(2 marks)**

c) Carbon dioxide is a greenhouse gas. Describe two reasons for increased carbon dioxide emissions over the last 200 years. **(2 marks)**

d) Some scientists dispute that global warming is taking place. Give one possible reason for this. **(1 mark)**

2 In recent years, as a result of international agreement, CFCs have been replaced by other chemicals in aerosol sprays and refrigerants. This is because the use of CFCs has been linked to a hole in the ozone layer.

a) Explain what the ozone layer is and why it is important. **(2 marks)**

b) Describe one of the likely consequences to humans of damage to the ozone layer. **(2 marks)**

c) Explain how CFCs are thought to have caused a hole in the ozone layer. **(2 marks)**

Score   / 13

Physics

How well did you do?

| 0–8 | Try again | 9–14 | Getting there | 15–20 | Good work | 21–26 | Excellent! |

For more information on this topic, see pages 72–73 of your Success Revision Guide.

The Solar System and Scale

Multiple-choice questions

Choose just one answer: A, B, C or D.

1 Which of the following planets is furthest from Earth? **(1 mark)**
- **A** Jupiter
- **B** Mercury
- **C** Neptune
- **D** Mars

2 Which is the only star in the Solar System? **(1 mark)**
- **A** Moon
- **B** Earth
- **C** Sun
- **D** Halley's comet

3 Approximately how old is the Solar System thought to be? **(1 mark)**

- **A** 5 000 000 000 000 years old
- **B** 5 000 000 000 years old
- **C** 5 000 000 years old
- **D** 5 000 years old

4 At what speed does light travel through space? **(1 mark)**
- **A** 3000 km/s
- **B** 300 000 km/s
- **C** 300 km/s
- **D** 3 000 000 km/s

5 Which of the following planets is closest to the Sun? **(1 mark)**
- **A** Jupiter
- **B** Mercury
- **C** Saturn
- **D** Neptune

Score   / 5

Short-answer questions

1 Put the following in order of increasing size: **(4 marks)**

- **A** The distance from the Earth to the Sun
- **B** The distance from the Earth to the Moon
- **C** The estimated diameter of our galaxy
- **D** 1 light year
- **E** The distance to the 'nearby' star Alpha Centauri

2 Draw one line from each type of body found in the Solar System to the most accurate description. **(4 marks)**

Sun	A natural satellite in orbit around a planet
Moon	A small rock, usually from a comet, entering the Earth's atmosphere
Asteroid	The star at the centre of the Solar System
Comet	A rock, up to about 1 km in diameter, in orbit around the Sun
Meteor	Accumulated ice and dust, with a nucleus that vaporises when it comes close the Sun

Score   / 8

Answer all parts of all questions. Continue on a separate sheet of paper if necessary.

1 The following data are for the orbital periods and surface temperature of planets in the Solar System.

	Distance from Sun (1×10^6 km)	Orbital period	Average surface temperature (°C) (on side facing Sun)
Mercury	60	88 days	430
Venus	110	220 days	470
Earth	150	365 1/4 days	20
Mars	230	2 years	−20
Jupiter	780	12 years	−150
Saturn	1400	30 years	−180
Uranus	2900	84 years	−210
Neptune	4500	160 years	−220

a) On the grid, plot a graph for average surface temperature against distance from Sun. **(4 marks)**

b) Explain the relationship between surface temperature and orbital distance. **(2 marks)**

....

....

c) State which planet is anomalous for this graph **(1 mark)**

....

....

d) Suggest one reason for this anomaly. **(1 mark)**

....

....

Score   / 8

How well did you do?

| 0–5 | Try again | 6–11 | Getting there | 12–16 | Good work | 17–21 | Excellent! |

For more information on this topic, see pages 74–75 of your Success Revision Guide.

Galaxies and Red-Shift

Multiple-choice questions

Choose just one answer: A, B, C or D.

1 What is the name of our galaxy? **(1 mark)**
  A Hubble   **B** Milky Way
  C Halley   **D** Andromeda

2 Who discovered the red-shift of distant galaxies? **(1 mark)**
  A Curtis   **B** Doppler
  C Hubble   **D** Shapley

3 What 'colour shift' would we expect for an object moving towards us very quickly? **(1 mark)**
  A red shift, due to increased apparent wavelength
  B blue shift, due to reduced apparent wavelength
  C red shift, due to reduced apparent wavelength
  D blue shift, due to increased apparent wavelength

4 Estimating the speed of a star relies on: **(1 mark)**
  A determination of the star's brightness
  B analysis of the star's emission spectrum
  C determination of the star's colour
  D analysis of the star's absorption spectrum

5 What is the name given to the effect which leads to the changing pitch of a moving police car siren? **(1 mark)**
  A Shapley Effect   **B** Hubble Effect
  C Doppler Effect   **D** Andromeda Effect

Score   / 5

Short-answer questions

1 a) Describe how the speed of a galaxy moving away from us changes with distance. (1 mark)

....

b) Describe how the effect described in part **a)** is useful to astronomers who discover distant galaxies. (1 mark)

....

....

2 Fill in the blank spaces using the terms in the box below. (8 marks)

bigger	closer	Doppler effect	blue	faster	Big Bang
slower	expanding	away	smaller	green	further

Observation of light from distant galaxies shows that the universe is ....

This provides evidence for the .... theory. The .... the galaxy, the

.... the red-shift, so the .... the galaxy is moving ....

This is an example of the .... If a galaxy were moving towards us, the light

would be ....-shifted.

Score   / 10

Answer all parts of all questions. Continue on a separate sheet of paper if necessary.

1 In the 1920s there was a great debate among astronomers about whether the Milky Way was one of many galaxies or the only galaxy.

a) Explain why scientists sometimes disagree about an explanation although they have seen the same data. **(2 marks)**

....

....

b) When further data become available it is often possible to eliminate some explanations and refine others.

Describe three processes undertaken by the scientific community to evaluate such data. **(3 marks)**

....

....

....

c) In the 1920s Harlow Shapley argued that the Milky Way was the only galaxy and that spiral nebulae were gas clouds. Heber Curtis argued that spiral nebulae were distant galaxies.

Tick the statements below that are true and that show how Edwin Hubble produced evidence to support Curtis's theory. **(1 mark)**

A He used a new telescope to observe the spiral nebulae. ☐
B He used red-shift to help measure distances. ☐
C He argued that you would not be able to see spiral nebulae if they were gas clouds. ☐
D He proved that the spiral nebulae contained solid matter. ☐
E He showed that spiral nebulae were outside the Milky Way and, therefore, could be other galaxies. ☐

2 ✎ Explain how the spectrum of light from distant stars enables us to identify the elements present in them and determine the speed at which they are moving towards, or away from, the Earth. **(6 marks)**

....

....

....

....

....

....

....

Score   / 12

Physics

How well did you do?

| 0–6 | Try again | 7–13 | Getting there | 14–20 | Good work | 21–27 | Excellent! |

For more information on this topic, see pages 76–77 of your Success Revision Guide.

Expanding Universe and Big Bang

Multiple-choice questions

Choose just one answer: A, B, C or D.

1 What observation supported the hypothesis that the Universe was initially very small and very hot? **(1 mark)**
- **A** The Big Bang
- **B** CMBR
- **C** red-shift
- **D** blue-shift

2 What attractive force prevents the Solar System from expanding? **(1 mark)**
- **A** blue-shift
- **B** The Big Bang
- **C** cosmic background
- **D** gravity

3 When do scientists think that the Big Bang happened? **(1 mark)**
- **A** 14 000 years ago
- **B** 14 000 000 years ago
- **C** 14 000 000 000 years ago
- **D** 14 000 000 000 000 years ago

4 What is a hypothesis? **(1 mark)**
- **A** a proven explanation for a phenomena
- **B** evidence to support a theory
- **C** a personal opinion
- **D** an explanation that takes account of limited data

5 The observations that Hubble made led him to conclude that: **(1 mark)**
- **A** the further away a galaxy is, the faster it is moving away
- **B** all galaxies are moving away at a constant speed
- **C** nearby galaxies are moving away faster than distant ones
- **D** most galaxies are stationary

Score   / 5

Short-answer questions

1 Draw a line to match each of Hubble's observations with the appropriate conclusion. **(3 marks)**

The distances to spiral nebulae are greater than the size of the Milky Way.	The further away a galaxy is, the faster it is moving.
The light from all the distant galaxies is red-shifted.	All the distant galaxies are moving away from us.
The further away the galaxy is, the bigger the red-shift.	Spiral nebulae are outside the Milky Way and are likely to be distant galaxies.

2 Use the words provided to complete the passage below. You may need to use some words more than once. **(6 marks)**

theory   radiation   confidence   hypothesis

The .... that the Universe started with a massive explosion led to the following

testable ....: The explosion produced .... that would now be found in

the microwave region of the spectrum. When data was found to support the ...., it

increased scientists' .... that the original .... provided a reliable

description of how the universe began.

Score   / 9

Answer all parts of all questions. Continue on a separate sheet of paper if necessary.

1 The following equation can be used to relate the red-shift to the speed (v) of a galaxy, where c (the speed of light) is 3×10^8 m/s:

$$\frac{\text{change in wavelength}}{\text{wavelength}} = \text{red-shift} = \frac{v}{c}$$

a) A galaxy gave a red-shift of 0.05

Calculate its speed. (2 marks)

....

....

b) If the red-shift in part **a)** was observed with radio waves of wavelength 5 m, calculate the change in wavelength observed. (2 marks)

....

....

c) The galaxy in part **a)** was 500 million light years away from Earth.

i) Tick the formula that shows the correct way to calculate this distance in metres. (1 mark)

A $500 \times 10^6 \times$ speed of light $\times$ seconds in a year ☐

B $500 \times 10^6 \times$ speed of light $\times$ days in a year ☐

C $500 \times$ speed of light $\times$ seconds in a year ☐

ii) Use the calculation you have selected to show that 500 million light years equates to approximately 5×10^{24} m. (2 marks)

....

....

....

d) Describe what is meant by the 'Universe' and how red-shift data can be used to estimate its age. (3 marks)

....

....

....

Score   / 10

Physics

How well did you do?

| 0–6 | Try again | 7–12 | Getting there | 13–18 | Good work | 19–24 | Excellent! |

For more information on this topic, see pages 78–79 of your Success Revision Guide.

Atoms and Elements

Multiple-choice questions

Choose just one answer: A, B, C or D.

1 Which particle found in an atom has no charge? **(1 mark)**
- **A** electron
- **B** neutron
- **C** nucleon
- **D** proton

2 What is the mass number of an atom? **(1 mark)**
- **A** number of neutrons
- **B** number of neutrons − number of electrons
- **C** number of neutrons + number of protons
- **D** number of protons

3 What do the two atoms $^{31}_{15}P$ and $^{32}_{16}S$ have in common? The same number of: **(1 mark)**

- **A** neutrons and protons
- **B** neutrons
- **C** protons and electrons
- **D** protons

4 What is the total number of protons in one molecule of water? **(1 mark)**
- **A** 9
- **B** 10
- **C** 17
- **D** 18

5 Which of these is the correct chemical symbol for sodium? **(1 mark)**
- **A** S
- **B** So
- **C** N
- **D** Na

Score   / 5

Short-answer questions

1 Complete the following passage. (8 marks)

All atoms are made up of a small dense nucleus. Surrounding the nucleus are ....

Most atoms contain three different particles: protons, ... and electrons.

.... are positively charged and have a relative mass of ....

.... are negatively charged and .... have no charge. All atoms of the same

element contain the same number of .... and ....

2 This is the information for the element tungsten, as it appears in the periodic table:

a) What is the mass number for tungsten? .... (1 mark)

b) What is the atomic number for tungsten? .... (1 mark)

```
184
W
tungsten
74
```

c) Describe the atomic structure of tungsten in terms of the number of protons, neutrons and electrons it has. (3 marks)

....

....

Score   / 13

Answer all parts of all questions. Continue on a separate sheet of paper if necessary.

1 Complete the table below, which is about the three types of particle found in an atom. **(3 marks)**

	Relative mass	Relative charge	Where found in the atom
electron			
proton			
neutron			

2 The diagram represents an atom of lithium (Li).

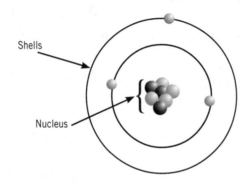

Shells

Nucleus

    a) What is represented by each of the symbols? **(3 marks)**

        i) grey dot ....

        ii) red dot ....

        iii) green dot ....

    b) What are shells? **(2 marks)**

    ....

    ....

    c) Explain why lithium has a mass number of 7 and an atomic number of 3. **(2 marks)**

    ....

    ....

    ....

    d) Write the symbol for lithium showing the mass number and atomic number. **(1 mark)**

    ....

Score   / 11

Chemistry

How well did you do?

| 0–7 | Try again | 8–14 | Getting there | 15–21 | Good work | 22–29 | Excellent! |

For more information on this topic, see pages 82–83 of your Success Revision Guide.

Formulae and Equations

Multiple-choice questions

Choose just one answer: A, B, C or D.

1 What is a compound? **(1 mark)**
   A two or more types of atom mixed together
   B two or more types of atom chemically combined
   C two or more atoms of the same element joined together
   D atoms of the same element with different mass numbers

2 Which of the following is NOT a state symbol? **(1 mark)**
   A (s) solid
   B (g) gaseous
   C (f) fluid
   D (aq) aqueous

3 What is the ratio of atoms in CO_2? **(1 mark)**
   A two carbon, two oxygen
   B two cobalt

   C one copper, two oxygen
   D one carbon, two oxygen

4 What is the ratio of atoms in $Ca(OH)_2$? **(1 mark)**
   A one calcium, one oxygen and two hydrogen
   B two calcium, two oxygen and two hydrogen
   C one calcium, two oxygen and two hydrogen
   D two calcium, one oxygen and one hydrogen

5 The law of conservation of mass states that: **(1 mark)**
   A the mass of the reactants is always greater than the mass of the products
   B the mass of the products is always greater than the mass of the reactants
   C the mass of the products of a chemical reaction is always the same
   D the mass of the reactants is always the same as the mass of the products

Score   / 5

Short-answer questions

1 Which elements are present in NH_4OH, and in what ratio? (2 marks)

2 Does 'CO' represent an element or a compound? Explain how you can tell. (2 marks)

3 What must sulfur trioxide, SO_3, react with to make sulfuric acid, H_2SO_4? (2 marks)

4 Write out in full all the information that is given by the following symbol equation:

$$2Mg(s) + O_2(g) \rightarrow 2MgO(s)$$ (9 marks)

Score   / 15

GCSE-style questions

Answer all parts of all questions. Continue on a separate sheet of paper if necessary.

 CO_2 H_2O NaCl SO_2 CuO NH_3

1 a) What do these six substances have in common? (2 marks)

....

....

b) i) Which formula represents the compound sodium chloride? (1 mark)

....

ii) Which formula represents the compound copper oxide? (1 mark)

....

c) Which two substances are 'dioxides'? How can you tell? (2 marks)

....

....

d) Give two reasons why the formula H_2O is more useful to a scientist than the name 'water'. (2 marks)

....

....

e) What information is given by the formula NH_3? (2 marks)

....

....

Score   / 10

How well did you do?

| 0–7 | Try again | 8–15 | Getting there | 16–23 | Good work | 24–30 | Excellent! |

For more information on this topic, see pages 84–85 of your Success Revision Guide.

Balancing Equations and Gas Tests

Multiple-choice questions

Choose just one answer: A, B, C or D.

Questions 1–3 refer to the unbalanced equation:

$Na(s) + Cl_2(g) \longrightarrow NaCl(s)$

1 What is the BEST meaning of the $\longrightarrow$ symbol? **(1 mark)**
- **A** is formed from
- **B** reacts to form
- **C** will become
- **D** will make

2 What do the symbols 's' and 'g' represent? **(1 mark)**
- **A** how reactive the chemicals are
- **B** the state symbols of the chemicals
- **C** the structure of the chemicals
- **D** the type of bonding in the chemicals

3 Which reaction is correctly balanced? **(1 mark)**
- **A** $2Na(s) + Cl_2(g) \longrightarrow 2NaCl(s)$
- **B** $2Na(s) + Cl_2(g) \longrightarrow Na_2Cl_2(s)$
- **C** $Na(s) + Cl(g) \longrightarrow NaCl(s)$
- **D** $Na(s) + Cl_2(g) \longrightarrow NaCl_2(s)$

4 Which gas turns limewater cloudy? **(1 mark)**
- **A** carbon dioxide
- **B** chlorine
- **C** hydrogen
- **D** oxygen

5 Which of the following describes the test for chlorine gas? **(1 mark)**
- **A** a lighted splint burns with a squeaky pop
- **B** a glowing splint relights
- **C** damp red litmus paper turns blue
- **D** damp litmus paper is bleached

Score   / 5

Short-answer questions

1 Balance the following equations. You will not have to write a number in every space.   **(6 marks)**

a) .... $H_2(g) +$ .... $O_2(g) \longrightarrow$ .... $H_2O(l)$

b) .... $C(s) +$ .... $CO_2(g) \longrightarrow$ .... $CO(g)$

c) .... $Cl_2(g) +$ .... $KBr(aq) \longrightarrow$ .... $Br_2(l) +$ .... $KCl(aq)$

d) .... $N_2(g) +$ .... $H_2(g) \longrightarrow$ .... $NH_3(g)$

e) .... $CH_4(g) +$ .... $O_2(g) \longrightarrow$ .... $CO_2(g) +$ .... $H_2O(g)$

f) .... $CuO(s) +$ .... $NH_3(g) \longrightarrow$ .... $Cu(s) +$ .... $H_2O(l) +$ .... $N_2(g)$

Score   / 6

Answer all parts of all questions. Continue on a separate sheet of paper if necessary.

1 Fill in the gaps by choosing from the following words. **(6 marks)**

elements   atoms   number   one   products   sides   state   three

There are four steps in writing a balanced chemical equation.

1. Write down the correct formulae of the reactants and ....

2. Check the number of .... of each element on both ....
of the equation.

3. Balance the equation by placing a .... in front of the formulae of

the substances in the equation. The number .... is not written.

4. Include the .... symbols in the equation.

2 The chemical reaction for the respiration of glucose ($C_6H_{12}O_6$) is

$$C_6H_{12}O_6(s) + 6O_2(g) \longrightarrow 6CO_2(g) + 6H_2O(g)$$

a) i) What is the total number of carbon atoms, hydrogen atoms and oxygen atoms
on the left hand side of the equation? **(1 mark)**

carbon atoms: .... hydrogen atoms: ....

oxygen atoms: ....

ii) What is the total number of carbon atoms, hydrogen atoms and

oxygen atoms on the right hand side of the equation? **(1 mark)**

carbon atoms: .... hydrogen atoms: ....

oxygen atoms: ....

b) State, giving a reason, whether or not the equation is balanced. **(2 marks)**

....

....

c) Describe the test that could be carried out in a laboratory to confirm that carbon dioxide is one
of the products of this reaction. **(2 marks)**

....

....

....

Score   / 12

Chemistry

How well did you do?

| 0–5 | Try again | 6–11 | Getting there | 12–17 | Good work | 18–23 | Excellent! |

For more information on this topic, see pages 86–87 of your Success Revision Guide.

Ionic and Covalent Bonding

Multiple-choice questions

Choose just one answer: A, B, C or D.

1 What name is given to a charged particle? **(1 mark)**
 A atom
 B ion
 C ionic
 D molecule

2 Which pair of elements is most likely to form a covalent compound? **(1 mark)**
 A calcium and oxygen
 B magnesium and oxygen
 C magnesium and sulfur
 D sulfur and oxygen

3 What is a 'cation'? **(1 mark)**
 A a metal atom that has lost one or more electrons
 B a metal atom that has gained one or more electrons
 C a non-metal atom that has gained one or more electrons
 D a non-metal atom with a negative charge

4 Which substance has the electronic structure shown in the diagram? **(1 mark)**

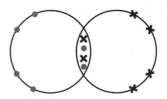

 A hydrogen (H_2)
 B hydrogen chloride (HCl)
 C oxygen (O_2)
 D sodium chloride (NaCl)

5 How many electrons are transferred when magnesium reacts with oxygen to form the ionic compound MgO? **(1 mark)**
 A 1
 B 2
 C 3
 D 4

Score / 5

Short-answer questions

1 The diagram shows the arrangement of electrons in a molecule of methane (CH_4).

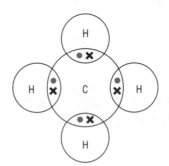

 a) How many: **(4 marks)**

 i) electrons are there in an atom of hydrogen

 ii) electrons are there in an atom of carbon

 iii) covalent bonds are there in a molecule of methane

 iv) shared pairs of electrons are there in a molecule of methane?

 b) Lithium contains 3 electrons and fluorine contains 9 electrons. On a separate sheet of paper, draw a diagram to show the arrangement of electrons and the type of bonding in lithium fluoride. **(3 marks)**

Score / 7

Answer all parts of all questions. Continue on a separate sheet of paper if necessary.

1 The diagram shows the arrangement of
electrons in a compound, P.

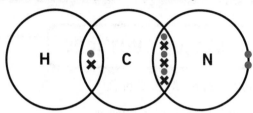

   a) Name the elements present in compound P. (3 marks)

   ....

   b) How many single covalent bonds can be formed by: (3 marks)

   i) hydrogen ....

   ii) carbon ....

   iii) nitrogen? ....

   c) The bonds between carbon and nitrogen are not single covalent bonds. Suggest
   how they might be described. (1 mark)

   ....

2 Element Y reacts with chlorine to form an ionic compound, YCl_2.

   a) Is Y a metal or a non-metal? Give a reason for your answer. (1 mark)

   ....

   b) i) What is the charge on ion Y in the compound YCl_2? .... (1 mark)

   ii) Y reacts with oxygen to form an oxide. Deduce the formula of the oxide. (1 mark)

   ....

   c) Chlorine can also form covalent bonds. Draw a dot-and-cross diagram of a covalent molecule of
   chlorine, Cl_2. (3 marks)

Score   / 13

Chemistry

How well did you do?

| 0–6 | Try again | | 7–13 | Getting there | | 14–20 | Good work | | 21–25 | Excellent! |

For more information on this topic, see pages 88–89 of your Success Revision Guide.

Plate Tectonics

Multiple-choice questions

Choose just one answer: A, B, C or D.

1 The layer under the Earth's crust is called: **(1 mark)**
- **A** the magma
- **B** the inner core
- **C** the outer core
- **D** the mantle

2 Who proposed the theory of 'continental drift'? **(1 mark)**
- **A** Albert Einstein
- **B** Charles Darwin
- **C** Alfred Wegener
- **D** Dimitri Mendeleev

3 How many plates is the Earth's crust divided into? **(1 mark)**
- **A** 12
- **B** 24
- **C** 55
- **D** over 100

4 Which of these would NOT be associated with the convergence of tectonic plates? **(1 mark)**
- **A** earthquakes
- **B** mid-oceanic ridges
- **C** volcanoes
- **D** tsunamis

5 What is the Earth's lithosphere? **(1 mark)**
- **A** the crust and upper mantle
- **B** the mantle and core
- **C** all the oceans and rivers
- **D** the lower atmosphere

Score   / 5

Short-answer questions

1 On the diagram, label the structural features of the Earth.

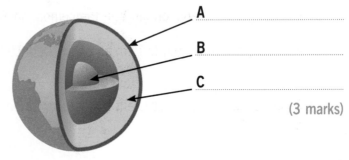

A ....

B ....

C ....

(3 marks)

2 What causes the Earth's plates to move? (2 marks)

3 What is the difference between magma and lava? (2 marks)

4 How is the oceanic crust different to the continental crust? (2 marks)

Score   / 9

Answer all parts of all questions. Continue on a separate sheet of paper if necessary.

1 The diagram shows an artist's impression of how the Earth's continents may once have been joined together in a supercontinent called Pangea. Alfred Wegener proposed that this supercontinent split and has drifted apart.

a) What evidence, provided by the shapes of continents, supports Wegener's theory?   **(2 marks)**

b) How did the discovery of certain types of fossil support Wegener's theory?   **(2 marks)**

c) Why were people reluctant to accept Wegener's theory when it was first proposed?   **(3 marks)**

d) Why was Wegener not able to demonstrate that the continents were moving?   **(1 mark)**

e) How can rocks that would have been formed by tropical swamps exist in Britain?   **(2 marks)**

Score   / 10

How well did you do?

| 0–6 | Try again | 7–12 | Getting there | 13–18 | Good work | 19–24 | Excellent! |

For more information on this topic, see pages 90–91 of your Success Revision Guide.

Evolution of the Atmosphere

Multiple-choice questions

Choose just one answer: A, B, C or D.

1 Which of these gases is NOT a component of today's atmosphere? **(1 mark)**

  A hydrogen

  B nitrogen

  C oxygen

  D argon

2 Which of these changes has happened since the Earth's early atmosphere? **(1 mark)**

  A the amount of methane has increased

  B green plants have increased carbon dioxide levels

  C bacteria have turned ammonia into nitrogen

  D volcanoes have released large quantities of oxygen

3 Which of these processes removes carbon dioxide from the atmosphere? **(1 mark)**

  A photosynthesis by green plants

  B respiration by living organisms

  C combustion of fuels

  D the action of soil bacteria

4 Which of these processes increases the amount of atmospheric carbon dioxide? **(1 mark)**

  A marine creatures making shells from calcium carbonate

  B volcanic eruptions

  C damage to the ozone layer

  D generation of electricity in nuclear power stations

5 What is the useful function of the ozone layer in the upper atmosphere? **(1 mark)**

  A it absorbs carbon dioxide from the atmosphere

  B it filters out harmful ultraviolet rays

  C it keeps the Earth's atmosphere cool

  D it releases oxygen into the atmosphere

Score / 5

Short-answer questions

1 Label, on the pie-chart, the two main gases present in today's atmosphere. **(2 marks)**

2 Oxygen was not present in the Earth's early atmosphere. Explain how it has been produced since then. **(2 marks)**

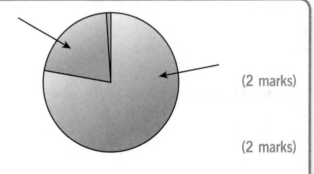

3 The early Earth had no water on its surface. Explain how the oceans are believed to have formed. **(2 marks)**

4 Earth's early atmosphere contained the gases methane and ammonia. What are the chemical formulae of these gases? **(2 marks)**

5 What is the chemical formula of ozone and in which part of the atmosphere is the ozone layer? **(2 marks)**

Score / 10

Answer all parts of all questions. Continue on a separate sheet of paper if necessary.

1 Earth's early atmosphere was thought to be mostly carbon dioxide, ammonia, water vapour and methane. All of these gases are 'greenhouse gases', so the temperature on the surface of the Earth would have been much higher than it is today.

a) Explain how early marine creatures reduced the amount of carbon dioxide in the atmosphere. **(2 marks)**

....

....

b) Explain what is meant when climate scientists tell us that much of the early Earth's carbon dioxide is now 'locked up in sedimentary rocks'. **(2 marks)**

....

....

....

c) What sort of living organism can release nitrogen into the atmosphere? **(2 marks)**

....

d) How have green plants affected Earth's atmosphere? **(2 marks)**

....

....

e) By what natural process, NOT involving living organisms, is the proportion of atmospheric carbon dioxide reduced? **(2 marks)**

....

....

....

....

Score   / 10

How well did you do?

| 0–6 | Try again | 7–12 | Getting there | 13–19 | Good work | 20–25 | Excellent! |

For more information on this topic, see pages 92–93 of your Success Revision Guide.

Atmospheric Gases

Multiple-choice questions

Choose just one answer: A, B, C or D.

1 What is air? **(1 mark)**
- **A** a compound
- **B** an element
- **C** a mixture of compounds
- **D** a mixture of elements and compounds

2 Which of the following gases is the LEAST common in air? **(1 mark)**
- **A** argon
- **B** carbon dioxide
- **C** oxygen
- **D** nitrogen

3 Which noble gas does NOT have eight electrons in its outer shell? **(1 mark)**
- **A** argon
- **B** helium
- **C** krypton
- **D** neon

4 Which gas is needed for combustion reactions to take place? **(1 mark)**
- **A** carbon dioxide
- **B** nitrogen
- **C** oxygen
- **D** argon

5 What type of bond occurs in Nitrogen (N_2) molecules? **(1 mark)**
- **A** ionic bond
- **B** single covalent bond
- **C** double covalent bond
- **D** triple covalent bond

Score / 5

Short-answer questions

1 a) Put the numbers below into their correct places in the following sentences. Each number may only be used once.

0   1   2   7   8

The noble gases are in group .... of the periodic table.

The elements after the noble gases are in group ....

All the noble gases, except helium, have .... electrons in their outer shell.

Helium has .... electrons in its outer shell. **(4 marks)**

b) Explain one practical use of the gas Helium. **(2 marks)**

....

....

Score / 6

Answer all parts of all questions. Continue on a separate sheet of paper if necessary.

1 The level of carbon dioxide in the atmosphere is relatively constant. The carbon cycle describes how carbon moves between the atmosphere, oceans and rocks.

a) State the chemical formula for carbon dioxide. **(1 mark)**

b) Tick the percentage that best describes the amount of carbon dioxide in the Earth's atmosphere today. **(1 mark)**

   A 78% ☐

   B 21% ☐

   C 1% ☐

   D less than 1% ☐

c) Name two processes by which carbon in plants and animals is released into the atmosphere. **(2 marks)**

d) Explain why plants play a critical role in maintaining the balance of atmospheric gases. **(2 marks)**

e) In some parts of the World large areas of forest are being cleared to make room for grazing for livestock. Some of the timber is then used for fuel. Explain how this practice is likely to impact the level of carbon dioxide in the atmosphere. **(3 marks)**

Score / 9

Chemistry

How well did you do?

| 0–5 | Try again | 6–10 | Getting there | 11–15 | Good work | 16–20 | Excellent! |

For more information on this topic, see pages 94–95 of your Success Revision Guide.

Pollution of the Atmosphere

Multiple-choice questions

Choose just one answer: A, B, C or D.

1 Which of these gases is produced by incomplete combustion of fuels? **(1 mark)**
   A methane
   B carbon monoxide
   C carbon dioxide
   D sulfur dioxide

2 Why should nitrogen oxides in exhaust gases be removed by catalytic converters? **(1 mark)**
   A they damage the ozone layer
   B they contribute to acid rain
   C they are the main cause of global warming
   D they are highly toxic and persist in the atmosphere

3 When a hydrocarbon fuel burns in sufficient oxygen: **(1 mark)**
   A carbon dioxide is the only product

   B no pollutant gases are produced
   C it produces the maximum possible heat energy
   D it produces dangerous toxic gases

4 What is caused by smoke particles in the atmosphere? **(1 mark)**
   A greenhouse effect
   B global warming
   C global dimming
   D acid rain

5 Which gas causes acid rain? **(1 mark)**
   A carbon dioxide
   B sulfur dioxide
   C carbon monoxide
   D methane

Score   / 5

Short-answer questions

1 Write a balanced symbol equation for burning sulfur in oxygen to produce sulfur dioxide. (2 marks)

2 Which environmental problems are caused by the production of sulfur dioxide and nitrogen oxides? (2 marks)

3 Give TWO reasons why it is better to burn fuels in a good supply of oxygen. (2 marks)

4 When a catalytic converter removes carbon monoxide and nitrogen oxides from exhaust fumes, what does it turn them into? (2 marks)

5 Why does the catalytic converter have a large internal surface area in contact with the exhaust gases? (2 marks)

Score   / 10

Answer all parts of all questions. Continue on a separate sheet of paper if necessary.

1 Many homes have their water heated by a gas boiler. It burns natural gas, which is mostly methane. The boiler supplies hot water to the radiators, as part of the central heating system. The boiler must be regularly serviced by a qualified gas engineer.

a) Write a balanced symbol equation for the burning of methane gas, CH_4, in sufficient oxygen for complete combustion. **(2 marks)**

....

b) If insufficient air is allowed into the boiler, incomplete combustion may happen. Why is this dangerous? **(2 marks)**

....

....

c) The boiler has a chimney, or flue, to allow the waste gases to go outside. Explain why we see white 'clouds' coming out of the flue when the boiler is operating. **(2 marks)**

....

....

d) Give three examples of checks you would expect the gas engineer to carry out when the boiler is serviced. **(3 marks)**

....

....

....

....

e) Most customers who buy a boiler of this type pay a yearly 'service contract' to a gas engineer. Suggest one benefit of this. **(1 mark)**

....

....

Score   / 10

How well did you do?

| 0–6 | Try again | 7–12 | Getting there | 13–19 | Good work | 20–25 | Excellent! |

For more information on this topic, see pages 96–97 of your Success Revision Guide.

Chemistry

Fuels

Multiple-choice questions

Choose just one answer: A, B, C or D.

1 Which of these is true, in general, if hydrocarbons have longer chains? **(1 mark)**
  A they are more viscous
  B they are easier to ignite
  C they have lower boiling points
  D they are more valuable as fuels

2 What is the main use for the kerosene fraction? **(1 mark)**
  A fuel for cars
  B fuel for aeroplanes
  C fuel for ships and power stations
  D used to surface roads

3 Which fuel contains mainly carbon? **(1 mark)**
  A natural gas
  B oil
  C coal
  D petrol

4 Which is not required for cracking? **(1 mark)**
  A a catalyst
  B a long-chain hydrocarbon
  C high pressure
  D high temperature

5 Fractional distillation works because: **(1 mark)**
  A hydrocarbons contain carbon and hydrogen
  B shorter alkanes are better fuels
  C there is a greater demand for alkenes
  D different hydrocarbons have different boiling points

Score   / 5

Short-answer questions

1 Why are fossil fuels said to be non-renewable? (2 marks)

2 Fill in the missing words to complete the description. (4 marks)

Crude oil is a .... of substances, the most important being .... It can

be separated into groups of molecules with a similar number of .... atoms. These

groups are called ....

3 Why do short-chain hydrocarbons make better fuels than long-chain hydrocarbons? (2 marks)

4 In the process of fractional distillation, which hydrocarbons rise furthest up the column? Explain your answer. (2 marks)

Score   / 10

Answer all parts of all questions. Continue on a separate sheet of paper if necessary.

1 **a)** Fill in the two missing labels on the diagram. (2 marks)

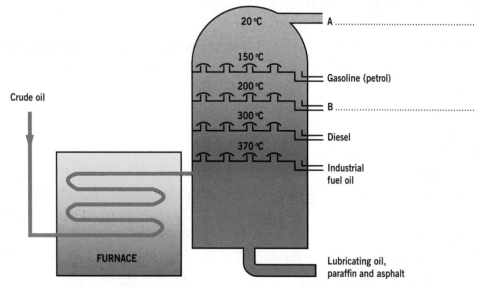

b) Explain how the fractionating column can separate the components of a mixture according to their different boiling points. (3 marks)

....

....

....

....

....

c) How can the oil refinery process the heavier fractions further, in order to improve profit? (2 marks)

....

....

d) Give one use for each of the following fractions:

i) kerosene (1 mark)

....

ii) bitumen (1 mark)

....

Score / 9

Chemistry

How well did you do?

| 0–6 | Try again | 7–12 | Getting there | 13–18 | Good work | 19–24 | Excellent! |

For more information on this topic, see pages 98–99 of your Success Revision Guide.

Organic Chemistry

Multiple-choice questions

Choose just one answer: A, B, C or D.

1 Which statement about the alkane homologous series is true? **(1 mark)**
- **A** they are all gases
- **B** they are all hydrocarbons
- **C** they are more reactive than the alkene
- **D** they are soluble in water

2 Which of the statements 1-3 are true for all alkenes? **(1 mark)**
1. They are all hydrocarbons.
2. They have the same empirical formula.
3. They have the same general formula.

- **A** 1 and 2 only
- **B** 1 and 3 only
- **C** 2 and 3 only
- **D** all three statements are correct

3 What is the best method to distinguish between an alkane and an alkene? **(1 mark)**
- **A** add bromine water
- **B** apply a lighted taper
- **C** add limewater
- **D** add pH indicator solution

4 How many bonds with other atoms can a single carbon atom form? **(1 mark)**
- **A** 1
- **B** 2
- **C** 4
- **D** 8

5 Which of the following statements are correct about saturated hydrocarbons?
1. They contain no double carbon-carbon bonds (C=C).
2. They contain the maximum number of hydrogen atoms.
3. They contain at least one oxygen atom. **(1 mark)**

- **A** 1 and 2 are correct
- **B** 1 and 3 are correct
- **C** 2 and 3 are correct
- **D** All three statements are correct

Score / 5

Short-answer questions

1 Complete the table below by filling in the gaps. (4 marks)

Alkane	Methane	Ethane	a)	Two isomers of butane	
		b)		c)	d)
Structural formula	H–C–H (with H above, below, left, right)		H–C–C–C–H (with H atoms)		

Score / 4

Answer all parts of all questions. Continue on a separate sheet of paper if necessary.

1 One of the reactions of decane ($C_{10}H_{22}$) is: $C_{10}H_{22} \longrightarrow C_6H_{14} + C_4H_8$

a) What name is given to this type of reaction? .... (1 mark)

b) i) Decane can break down to give one alkene molecule with 9 carbon atoms and X.

What is X? .... (2 marks)

ii) Decane can also break down to form one alkane molecule with 8 carbon atoms and Y.

What is Y? ....

c) How can X and Y be identified as an alkane and an alkene? (2 marks)

....

....

2 Both propane (C_3H_8) and butane (C_4H_{10}) are used in canisters for camping gas. The table shows the melting points and boiling points of ethane, propane and butane.

	Ethane	Propane	Butane
Melting point (°C)	−181	−187	−138
Boiling point (°C)	−89	−42	−0.5

a) What is the formula of: (2 marks)

i) ethane .... **ii)** pentane (an alkane with 5 carbon atoms)? ....

b) Suggest the boiling point of pentane. (1 mark)

....

c) Explain why a colourless liquid appears on the outside of a metal pot filled with cold water when it is first put on a camping gas fire. (2 marks)

....

d) Suggest why explorers take canisters of propane and not butane when they are on an expedition to the Antarctic. (2 marks)

....

....

Score / 12

How well did you do?

| 0–5 | Try again | 6–10 | Getting there | 11–15 | Good work | 16–21 | Excellent! |

For more information on this topic, see pages 100–101 of your Success Revision Guide.

Ethanol

Multiple-choice questions

Choose just one answer: A, B, C or D.

1 Which is true about ethane and
ethanol? **(1 mark)**
- **A** they are in the same physical state
at room temperature and pressure
- **B** they both react with sodium
- **C** they have the same number of
carbon atoms
- **D** they have the same relative
molecular mass

2 Which equation represents the complete
combustion of ethanol? **(1 mark)**
- **A** $2C_2H_5OH + 3O_2 \longrightarrow 4CO_2 + 6H_2$
- **B** $C_2H_5OH + 3O_2 \longrightarrow 2CO_2 + 3H_2O$
- **C** $C_2H_5OH + 2O_2 \longrightarrow 2CO + 3H_2O$
- **D** $C_2H_5OH + O_2 \longrightarrow CH_3COOH + H_2O$

3 What is NOT a use of ethanol? **(1 mark)**
- **A** as a fuel
- **B** as a solvent
- **C** in alcoholic drinks
- **D** to remove blood stains

4 What is the role of yeast during
fermentation? **(1 mark)**
- **A** reactant
- **B** product
- **C** catalyst
- **D** emulsifier

5 What is the approximate concentration of
ethanol produced by fermentation? **(1 mark)**
- **A** 1–5%
- **B** 6–14%
- **C** 15–25%
- **D** 26%+

Score / 5

Short-answer questions

1 In Brazil, ethanol is produced as a biofuel for cars to reduce the country's dependency on
crude oil.

a) What raw material is ethanol made from as a biofuel? (1 mark)

b) i) Why is ethanol a renewable energy resource? (1 mark)

ii) Give one other advantage of ethanol over fossil fuels. (1 mark)

iii) Give one disadvantage of ethanol compared to fossil fuels. (1 mark)

Score / 4

Answer all parts of all questions. Continue on a separate sheet of paper if necessary.

1 The apparatus shown can be used to prepare ethanol from sugar.

a) i) What substances are placed in the flask? (2 marks)

....

ii) What substance is in the test tube to show that carbon dioxide is given off? (1 mark)

....

b) What is the best temperature range at which to perform this experiment? (1 mark)

....

c) Complete the equation below to represent the reaction taking place. (1 mark)

$C_6H_{12}O_6(aq) \longrightarrow 2C_2H_5OH +$ ....

d) How would you know that fermentation had finished? (1 mark)

....

e) Why is the ethanol in the flask NOT oxidised to ethanoic acid? (2 marks)

....

....

f) Ethanol can also be made from waste biomass.

i) What are the advantages of making ethanol from waste biomass? (2 marks)

....

....

ii) ✎ How is ethanol made from biomass and what chemicals and conditions are required?

(Answer on a separate sheet of paper.) (6 marks)

Score   / 16

How well did you do?

| 0–6 | Try again | 7–13 | Getting there | 14–19 | Good work | 20–25 | Excellent! |

For more information on this topic, see pages 102–103 of your Success Revision Guide.

Plastics

Multiple-choice questions

Choose just one answer: A, B, C or D.

1 What is a 'polymer'? **(1 mark)**
- **A** a hydrocarbon
- **B** a chain of monomers joined together
- **C** a thermoplastic material
- **D** a non-biodegradable material

2 Which of these polymers is the non-stick coating on pans? **(1 mark)**
- **A** PVC
- **B** polystyrene
- **C** polythene
- **D** PTFE

3 If polymer chains are cross-linked, the polymer will: **(1 mark)**
- **A** be a thermosetting material
- **B** have a lower melting point
- **C** be very flexible
- **D** be easier to mould into shape

4 What is the process called that examines the environmental impact of a product over its entire lifetime? **(1 mark)**
- **A** RCA
- **B** CCC
- **C** PVC
- **D** LCA

5 Which of these is NOT responsible for the properties of a polymer? **(1 mark)**
- **A** the type of monomer
- **B** the length of the polymer chains
- **C** the degree of cross-linking
- **D** the cost of manufacture

Score   / 5

Short-answer questions

1 Name TWO natural polymers. (2 marks)

2 Name one man-made polymer and the monomer it is made from. (2 marks)

3 Give TWO advantages that PVC guttering has over metal guttering. (2 marks)

4 How does crystallinity affect the properties of a plastic? (2 marks)

5 What properties of PTFE make it suitable for coating frying pans? (2 marks)

Score   / 10

Answer all parts of all questions. Continue on a separate sheet of paper if necessary.

1 Many household objects are made from polythene. A softened polythene sheet may be vacuum-formed into a shape, staying in that shape when the polythene cools. Polythene can have colouring pigments added to it to make brightly-coloured objects.

a) How is polythene made? (2 marks)

b) Polythene arrives at the factory as sacks of tiny granules. What has to be done to these granules to make the soft polythene sheet, ready for vacuum-forming? (1 mark)

c) Is polythene a thermoset or a thermoplastic material? Explain how you can tell. (2 marks)

d) What are the advantages of making a bucket out of polythene over the more traditional iron? (2 marks)

e) A polythene bucket has some plasticiser added to the polymer to make it less rigid. Why might this be necessary? (2 marks)

Score / 9

How well did you do?

| 0–6 Try again | 7–12 Getting there | 13–18 Good work | 19–24 Excellent! |

Chemistry

For more information on this topic, see pages 104–105 of your Success Revision Guide.

101

Vegetable Oils

Multiple-choice questions

Choose just one answer: A, B, C or D.

1 Why are most vegetable oils liquid at
room temperature? **(1 mark)**
- **A** they are fully saturated
- **B** they have C=C double-bonds
- **C** they are biodegradable
- **D** shorter-chain molecules have weak bonds

2 What is the by-product of
saponification? **(1 mark)**
- **A** glucose
- **B** glycerol
- **C** glycogen
- **D** ethanol

3 Which of these is used as the test for
unsaturated hydrocarbons? **(1 mark)**
- **A** bromine solution
- **B** starch solution

- **C** sodium carbonate solution
- **D** silver nitrate solution

4 Which of these processes would not use
vegetable oil? **(1 mark)**
- **A** production of biodiesel
- **B** production of soap
- **C** production of margarine
- **D** production of butter

5 A chemical that helps oil and water mix
is called: **(1 mark)**
- **A** an acid
- **B** an emulsifier
- **C** a catalyst
- **D** an antioxidant

Score / 5

Short-answer questions

1 Name TWO major sources of vegetable oil. (2 marks)

2 Why are vegetable oils usually liquid, whilst animal fats tend to be solid? (2 marks)

3 What colour change in bromine solution indicates that a fat molecule is unsaturated? (2 marks)

4 Why must vegetable oils be hydrogenated to make margarine? (2 marks)

5 What is the function of an emulsifier? (2 marks)

Score / 10

Answer all parts of all questions. Continue on a separate sheet of paper if necessary.

1 Margarine is an alternative to butter, and many brands claim to be 'high in polyunsaturates' and to 'help prevent heart-disease'.

a) What do you understand by the term 'polyunsaturates'? (2 marks)

....

....

....

b) What has been done to the vegetable oil in order to make it look and taste more like butter? (2 marks)

....

....

....

c) How does the number of C=C double bonds in the margarine compare with the number in the unprocessed vegetable oil? (1 mark)

....

....

d) Why might people prefer putting margarine onto bread, rather than vegetable oil? (2 marks)

....

....

....

e) What medical problems are associated with eating too much saturated fat? (2 marks)

....

....

....

....

....

Score   / 9

Chemistry

How well did you do?

| 0–6 | Try again | 7–12 | Getting there | 13–18 | Good work | 19–24 | Excellent! |

For more information on this topic, see pages 106–107 of your Success Revision Guide.

Iron and Steel

Multiple-choice questions

Choose just one answer: A, B, C or D.

1 Which substance is NOT an essential raw material in the manufacture of iron? **(1 mark)**
   A air
   B coke
   C limestone
   D sand

2 Which metal is found uncombined in the Earth's crust? **(1 mark)**
   A aluminium
   B gold
   C iron
   D sodium

3 Which element, together with iron, is always present in cast iron? **(1 mark)**
   A carbon
   B chromium

   C nickel
   D zinc

4 What is the main disadvantage of cast iron? **(1 mark)**
   A it has a low melting point
   B it is brittle
   C it is soft
   D it rusts very easily

5 What is an alloy? **(1 mark)**
   A a compound of metals with only metals
   B a compound of metals with other elements
   C a mixture of metals with only non-metals
   D a mixture of metals with other elements

Score   / 5

Short-answer questions

1 a) The flow diagram shows how iron is produced in the blast furnace.

Identify R, S and T.

R is ....

S is ....

(2 marks)

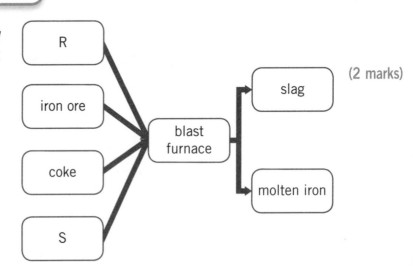

b) Explain why most of the iron made in a blast furnace is used to produce steel. **(2 marks)**

....

....

Score   / 4

GCSE-style questions

Answer all parts of all questions. Continue on a separate sheet of paper if necessary.

1 This experiment was designed to investigate the conditions necessary for rusting iron nails.

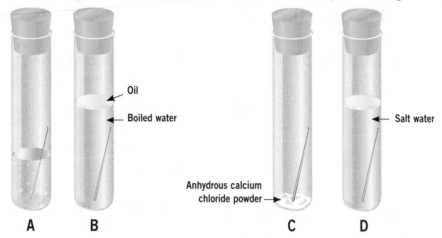

Oil

Boiled water

Salt water

Anhydrous calcium chloride powder →

A   **B**   **C**   **D**

a) i) Why does each test tube have a bung in the top? (1 mark)

....

ii) Why is oil placed on top of the water in test tube B? (1 mark)

....

iii) Why is the water in test tube B boiled? (1 mark)

....

iv) What is the purpose of the calcium chloride in test C? (1 mark)

....

b) Complete the table below. (4 marks)

Test tube	Is water present?	Is air present?	Observation
A		yes	rusts
B	yes		no rust
C			no rust
D			rusts very quickly

Score   / 8

How well did you do?

| 0–4 | Try again | 5–9 | Getting there | 10–13 | Good work | 14–17 | Excellent! |

For more information on this topic, see pages 108–109 of your Success Revision Guide.

Chemistry

Transition Metals

Multiple-choice questions

Choose just one answer: A, B, C or D.

1 Which element has the highest melting point? **(1 mark)**

- **A** aluminium
- **B** iron
- **C** magnesium
- **D** potassium

2 Which transition metal is used as a catalyst in the manufacture of margarine? **(1 mark)**

- **A** gold
- **B** iron
- **C** manganese
- **D** nickel

3 Which statement is true about both group 1 metals and transition metals? **(1 mark)**

- **A** they are good catalysts
- **B** they are good conductors of electricity
- **C** they are reactive metals
- **D** they have low melting points

4 Which statement about the transition metals is NOT true? **(1 mark)**

- **A** they are in period 3 of the periodic table
- **B** they form coloured compounds
- **C** they have higher melting points than group 1 metals
- **D** they occur between group 2 and group 3 in the periodic table

5 Which property of transition metals does NOT distinguish them from group 1 metals? **(1 mark)**

- **A** they are dense and tough
- **B** they are good catalysts
- **C** they are good conductors of heat and electricity
- **D** they have variable valencies

Score / 5

Short-answer questions

1 The table below gives the properties of three metals: R, S and T.

Metal	Density (g/cm³)	Reaction with cold water	Compound formed with chlorine	
			Formula	Colour of aqueous solution
R	1.74	very slowly	RCl_2	colourless
S	0.97	very fast	SCl	colourless
T	8.92	no reaction	TCl_2	blue/green

a) i) Which metal is a transition metal? .... **(1 mark)**

ii) Give TWO reasons for your answer. **(2 marks)**

....

....

b) Suggest identities for R, S and T. **(3 marks)**

R .... S .... T ....

Score / 6

Answer all parts of all questions. Continue on a separate sheet of paper if necessary.

1 Titanium is made from rutile (TiO_2) in two stages.

Stage 1: Chlorine is passed over a heated mixture of rutile and carbon. The products are titanium(IV) chloride ($TiCl_4$) and carbon monoxide.

a) i) Write the word equation for this reaction. **(1 mark)**

....

ii) Titanium dioxide has a giant molecular structure. Suggest TWO properties of titanium dioxide. **(2 marks)**

....

iii) Titanium(IV) chloride melts at –23°C. On a separate sheet of paper, draw a diagram to show the bonding in $TiCl_4$. Only show the electrons in the outer shell. (Titanium has four electrons in its outer shell.) **(2 marks)**

iv) Titanium(IV) chloride is separated from the mixture by fractional distillation. Explain what is meant by 'fractional distillation'. **(1 mark)**

....

....

Stage 2: Titanium tetrachloride is reduced to titanium by heating it with magnesium in an atmosphere of argon. The other product of the reaction is magnesium chloride.

b) i) Why is the reaction carried out in an atmosphere of argon? **(1 mark)**

....

ii) Write the balanced symbol equation, including state symbols, for the reaction between magnesium and titanium tetrachloride. **(3 marks)**

....

iii) How can magnesium and chlorine be obtained from the magnesium chloride produced in the above reaction, so that they can be recycled? **(1 mark)**

....

c) Titanium forms another chloride, titanium(III) chloride. This chloride is violet in colour. Give TWO properties of titanium that indicate that it is a transition metal. **(2 marks)**

....

Score   / 13

How well did you do?

| 0–6 | Try again | 7–12 | Getting there | 13–18 | Good work | 19–24 | Excellent! |

For more information on this topic, see pages 110–111 of your Success Revision Guide.

Chemistry

Copper

Multiple-choice questions

Choose just one answer: A, B, C or D.

1 The chemical symbol for copper is: **(1 mark)**
 A Co **B** Cp **C** Cr **D** Cu

2 Which alloy contains copper as the main constituent? **(1 mark)**
 A brass   **B** bronze
 C duralumin   **D** stainless steel

3 Which mineral is an ore containing copper? **(1 mark)**
 A bauxite   **B** haematite
 C malachite   **D** rutile

4 Which of the properties 1–3 make copper suitable for use as water pipes? **(1 mark)**
 1. anti-bacterial
 2. thermal conductor
 3. ductile
 A 1 and 2 only   **B** 1 and 3 only
 C 2 and 3 only   **D** all three properties

5 What are the advantages of extracting copper by bioleaching? **(1 mark)**
 A it is a slow process
 B it causes less environmental damage
 C the copper produced contains other elements
 D the products are toxic

Score   / 5

Short-answer questions

1 The diagram shows an experiment to show how copper can be purified.

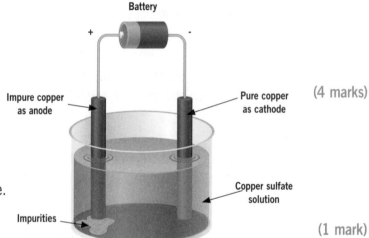

 a) Name the FOUR ions present in the copper(II) sulfate solution. **(4 marks)**

 ....

 ....

 b) Copper is deposited on the cathode. What does this tell you about the charge on the copper ion? **(1 mark)**

 ....

 c) Explain, with reasons, what happens to the blue colour of the copper(II) sulfate solution. **(3 marks)**

 ....

 ....

 d) What would be formed at the electrodes if carbon had been used as electrodes? **(2 marks)**

  i) at the anode ....   **ii)** at the cathode ....

Score   / 10

Answer all parts of all questions. Continue on a separate sheet of paper if necessary.

1 The main ore of copper is chalcopyrite ($CuFeS_2$). The traditional way of making copper is to roast this ore in air. The equation for the reaction is:

$$2CuFeS_2(s) + 4O_2(g) \longrightarrow Cu_2S(s) + 2FeO(s) + 3SO_2(g)$$

a) i) Write the word equation for the above reaction. **(3 marks)**

....

ii) Why is FeO formed and not CuO? **(1 mark)**

....

b) The iron(II) oxide is removed from the mixture by adding silicon dioxide and blowing air through the mixture. Iron is removed as a slag of iron(II) silicate. Copper(I) sulfide reacts with oxygen to form copper and sulfur dioxide.

i) Name another industrial process in which a silicate is formed as a waste product. **(1 mark)**

....

ii) Write the balanced symbol equation, including state symbols, for the formation of copper.**(2 marks)**

....

c) Copper forms a bright red oxide called copper(I) oxide.
Write the name, formula and colour of another oxide of copper. **(3 marks)**

....

....

d) From the above information, give TWO properties of copper which suggest that it is a transition metal. **(2 marks)**

....

....

e) Another ore of copper contains the mineral malachite. The formula of malachite is $CuCO_3Cu(OH)_2$

Which two gases would be given off if malachite was heated? **(2 marks)**

.... and ....

Score   / 14

How well did you do?

| 0–7 | Try again | 8–14 | Getting there | 15–21 | Good work | 22–29 | Excellent! |

For more information on this topic, see pages 112–113 of your Success Revision Guide.

Aluminium

Multiple-choice questions

Choose just one answer: A, B, C or D.

1 What is the main ore of aluminium? **(1 mark)**
- **A** bauxite
- **B** clay
- **C** cryolite
- **D** haematite

2 Which reaction takes place in the manufacture of aluminium? **(1 mark)**
- **A** aluminium ions accept electrons to form aluminium atoms
- **B** aluminium oxide is decomposed by heat
- **C** aluminium oxide is reduced by carbon
- **D** aluminium reacts with the graphite electrodes

3 Which of the following is NOT a property of aluminium alloys? **(1 mark)**
- **A** high strength
- **B** poor electrical conductor
- **C** low density
- **D** good electrical conductor

4 Which of the following substances, together with aluminium, are formed during the manufacture of aluminium? **(1 mark)**
1. carbon dioxide
2. oxygen
3. sodium

- **A** 1 and 2
- **B** 1 and 3
- **C** 2 and 3
- **D** all three substances are produced

5 From the chemistry of the manufacture of aluminium and iron, what is the order of reactivity of aluminium, carbon and iron towards oxygen? **(1 mark)**

	Most reactive		Least reactive
A	Al	C	Fe
B	Al	Fe	C
C	C	Al	Fe
D	C	Fe	Al

Score / 5

Short-answer questions

1 Fill in the gaps in the following paragraph. (6 marks)

Aluminium is the commonest .... in the Earth's crust. In nature, aluminium

is found only in chemical compounds such as ...., also known as impure hydrated

aluminium oxide. Aluminium is a reactive metal. It cannot be manufactured by reducing its oxide

with .... Instead it is made by the .... of aluminium oxide dissolved in

cryolite (sodium aluminium fluoride). Aluminium appears to be unreactive because it forms a

thin .... layer on its surface. This layer prevents the metal from coming into contact

with other chemicals. For example, aluminium .... are used for storing fizzy drinks.

Score / 6

Answer all parts of all questions. Continue on a separate sheet of paper if necessary.

1 The diagram shows how aluminium is extracted from its ore by electrolysis.

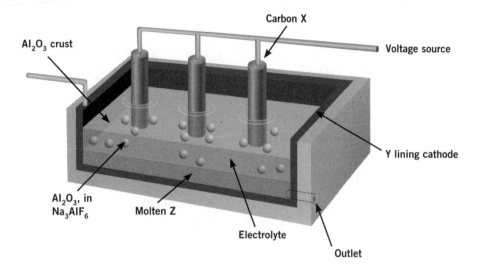

a) Identify X, Y and Z on the diagram. (3 marks)

X is: .... Y is: .... Z is: ....

b) What is meant by 'electrolysis'? (2 marks)

....

c) Give the formulae of THREE of the ions present in the electrolyte.

.... (3 marks)

d) The word equation for the reaction taking place in the cell is:

aluminium oxide ⟶ aluminium + oxygen

Use this equation to explain the meaning of 'reduction'. (2 marks)

....

....

e) Explain why the following help to make the extraction process economical:

i) the building of a hydroelectric power (HEP) station to supply the plant with electricity (1 mark)

....

ii) the presence of a crust of aluminium oxide on the molten electrolyte. (1 mark)

....

Score / 12

How well did you do?

0–6 | Try again   7–12 | Getting there   13–18 | Good work   19–23 | Excellent!

Chemistry

Limestone

Multiple-choice questions

Choose just one answer: A, B, C or D.

1 What are the products of the action of heat on calcium carbonate? **(1 mark)**
- **A** calcium carbide (Ca_2C) and oxygen
- **B** calcium oxide, carbon dioxide and oxygen
- **C** calcium oxide and carbon dioxide
- **D** calcium, carbon and oxygen

2 Which metal needs limestone in its manufacture? **(1 mark)**
- **A** aluminium
- **B** copper
- **C** iron
- **D** titanium

3 What is the ratio of the atoms in aluminium nitrate $Al_2(NO_3)_3$? **(1 mark)**

	Aluminium	Nitrogen	Oxygen
A	1	1	9
B	1	1	3
C	2	1	3
D	2	3	9

4 Which of the following is NOT a form of calcium carbonate? **(1 mark)**
- **A** alumina
- **B** chalk
- **C** limestone
- **D** marble

5 Which reaction produces calcium carbonate? **(1 mark)**
- **A** burning calcium in carbon dioxide
- **B** heating calcium, carbon and oxygen together
- **C** heating sodium carbonate with calcium
- **D** passing carbon dioxide into limewater

Score   / 5

Short-answer questions

1 Fill in the blanks. (6 marks)

a) Glass is made by heating limestone with .... and ....

b) Cement is made by roasting powdered limestone with powdered ....

c) Mortar is made when water is mixed with .... and sand.

d) Limestone is an example of .... rock.

e) Limestone is a strong building material because of the ordered arrangement of

.... in its crystal structure.

2 Name THREE materials that are made from living things. (3 marks)

....

....

Score   / 9

Answer all parts of all questions. Continue on a separate sheet of paper if necessary.

1 Limestone contains calcium carbonate. Calcium carbonate has the formula $CaCO_3$.

a) Complete the sentence by writing in the correct numbers. **(2 marks)**

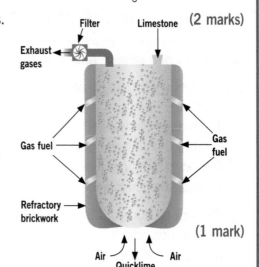

The formula of calcium carbonate is made up of

1 calcium atom, ... carbon atom(s) and

.... oxygen atom(s).

Calcium oxide is made by heating calcium carbonate to 900°C in a lime kiln. It forms one other compound.

$$CaCO_3(s) \longrightarrow CaO(s) + CO_2(g)$$

b) i) Give the chemical name of the solid product. **(1 mark)**

....

ii) What type of reaction is the action of heat on calcium carbonate? **(2 marks)**

....

c) i) Explain why the exhaust gases are filtered. **(1 mark)**

....

ii) Explain why nitrogen is present in the exhaust gases. **(2 marks)**

....

....

d) Suggest one important property of the refractory brickwork. **(1 mark)**

....

e) i) When water is added to quicklime an alkali is formed. What is **i)** the name of the alkali and **ii)** the formula of the alkali? **(2 marks)**

i) ....   ii) ....

iii) What type of soil might benefit from the addition of quicklime and what would the quicklime do? **(2 marks)**

....

f) Strontium (Sr) is in the same group as calcium. Write the formula of: **(2 marks)**

i) strontium hydroxide ....   ii) strontium sulfate ....

Score   / 15

Chemistry

How well did you do?

| 0–7 | Try again | 8–14 | Getting there | 15–21 | Good work | 22–29 | Excellent! |

For more information on this topic, see pages 116–117 of your Success Revision Guide.

Salts and Metal Carbonates

Multiple-choice questions

Choose just one answer: A, B, C or D.

1 A reaction between an acid and an alkali: (1 mark)
- **A** produces only water
- **B** always produces a salt
- **C** always produces hydrogen
- **D** always requires energy

2 The salt produced by reacting copper oxide and sulfuric acid is: (1 mark)
- **A** copper sulfate
- **B** sodium chloride
- **C** copper sulfide
- **D** copper sulfite

3 Which of the following is NOT a product of a reaction between a metal carbonate and an acid? (1 mark)
- **A** a salt
- **B** water
- **C** hydrogen
- **D** carbon dioxide

4 Mixing barium chloride and sodium sulfate solutions produces which of the following? (1 mark)
- **A** the insoluble salt, sodium chloride
- **B** a soluble salt and water
- **C** a neutralisation reaction
- **D** the insoluble salt, barium sulfate

5 Which gas is produced when metals react with acids? (1 mark)
- **A** carbon dioxide
- **B** hydrogen
- **C** oxygen
- **D** nitrogen

Score / 5

Short-answer questions

1 Write a balanced symbol equation for the reaction between hydrochloric acid (HCl) and sodium hydroxide (NaOH). (2 marks)

2 What would be the products of the reaction between calcium oxide and nitric acid? (2 marks)

3 What gas is produced when magnesium reacts with sulfuric acid and how might you identify it? (2 marks)

4 What is the colour change that takes place when copper(II) carbonate is heated to produce copper oxide? (2 marks)

5 Give the name and formula of the salt formed when zinc carbonate reacts with sulfuric acid. (2 marks)

Score / 10

GCSE-style questions

Answer all parts of all questions. Continue on a separate sheet of paper if necessary.

1 This question is about the preparation of copper(II) sulfate crystals.

a) One spatula full of powdered copper(II) carbonate is added to about $50\,cm^3$ of dilute sulfuric acid. A gas is given off and the mixture gets warm.

  i) What gas is given off? .... (1 mark)

  ii) What name is given to a reaction that gives off heat? .... (1 mark)

  iii) Why is *powdered* copper(II) carbonate used? (1 mark)

  ....

b) Copper(II) carbonate is added until there is no further reaction.

  Give TWO observations that indicate that the reaction has finished.

  i) .... (1 mark)

  ii) .... (1 mark)

c) The mixture is filtered and the filtrate collected in an evaporating basin.

  Why is the mixture filtered? (1 mark)

  ....

d) The filtrate is boiled until it becomes saturated.

  What is the meaning of the following words?

  i) filtrate .... (1 mark)

  ii) saturated .... (1 mark)

e) Crystals form if the filtrate is left in a warm place for several days.

  What has been lost from the evaporating basin during this time? (1 mark)

  ....

f) Write **i)** the word equation and **ii)** the balanced symbol equation, including state symbols, for the above experiment.

  i) .... (1 mark)

  ii) .... (2 marks)

Score   / 12

How well did you do?

| 0–6 | Try again | 7–13 | Getting there | 14–20 | Good work | 21–27 | Excellent! |

For more information on this topic, see pages 118–119 of your Success Revision Guide.

The Electrolysis of Sodium Chloride Solution

Multiple-choice questions

Choose just one answer: A, B, C or D.

1 Which of these is an important use of chlorine? **(1 mark)**
- **A** flavouring food
- **B** making bleach
- **C** making margarine
- **D** as an industrial alkali

2 What is produced when sodium chloride solution is electrolysed? **(1 mark)**
- **A** sodium and chlorine only
- **B** hydrogen and chlorine only
- **C** chlorine and water only
- **D** sodium hydroxide, hydrogen and chlorine

3 What happens when sodium chloride solution is electrolysed? **(1 mark)**
- **A** hydrogen ions are oxidised
- **B** chloride ions are reduced
- **C** chloride ions are oxidised
- **D** sodium ions are reduced

4 What is the substance that is broken down in electrolysis called? **(1 mark)**
- **A** cryolite
- **B** cation
- **C** electrode
- **D** electrolyte

5 The particles that move when a substance is electrolysed are: **(1 mark)**
- **A** molecules
- **B** delocalised electrons
- **C** ions
- **D** atoms

Score   / 5

Short-answer questions

1 Why is salt spread onto roads in winter? (2 marks)

2 Why is the electrolysis of sodium chloride solution an important industrial process? (3 marks)

3 Why are the electrodes used in the electrolysis of sodium chloride solution made from inert materials? (1 mark)

4 What term describes a reaction where a positive ion gains electrons? (1 mark)

5 What term describes a reaction where a negative ion loses electrons? (1 mark)

Score   / 8

Answer all parts of all questions. Continue on a separate sheet of paper if necessary.

1 This apparatus can be used to electrolyse a solution of sodium chloride in the laboratory. When the current is flowing, bubbles of gas can be seen rising from both electrodes and the electrolyte becomes alkaline. This apparatus is a small-scale version of a major industrial process.

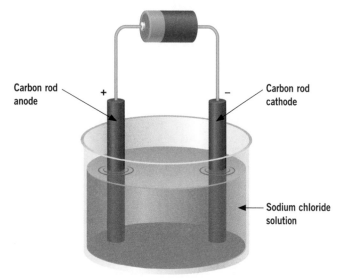

Carbon rod anode   +   −   Carbon rod cathode

Sodium chloride solution

a) Which TWO gases are produced when sodium chloride is electrolysed? **(2 marks)**

....

b) What happens to the chloride ions when they reach the positive electrode (anode)? **(2 marks)**

....

....

c) Why does the electrolyte become alkaline? **(2 marks)**

....

....

d) Write a symbol equation to show the reduction of hydrogen ions at the cathode. **(2 marks)**

....

e) Give TWO examples of products which use chlorine gas in their manufacture. **(2 marks)**

....

....

Score   / 10

How well did you do?

| 0–5 | Try again | | 6–11 | Getting there | | 12–17 | Good work | | 18–23 | Excellent! |

For more information on this topic, see pages 120–121 of your Success Revision Guide.

117

Notes

Notes

Periodic Table

Key

| relative atomic mass |
| **atomic symbol** |
| name |
| atomic (proton) number |

| 1 | H | hydrogen | 1 |

Group 1	Group 2											Group 3	Group 4	Group 5	Group 6	Group 7	Group 0
																	4 **He** helium 2
7 **Li** lithium 3	9 **Be** beryllium 4											11 **B** boron 5	12 **C** carbon 6	14 **N** nitrogen 7	16 **O** oxygen 8	19 **F** fluorine 9	20 **Ne** neon 10
23 **Na** sodium 11	24 **Mg** magnesium 12											27 **Al** aluminium 13	28 **Si** silicon 14	31 **P** phosphorus 15	32 **S** sulfur 16	35.5 **Cl** chlorine 17	40 **Ar** argon 18
39 **K** potassium 19	40 **Ca** calcium 20	45 **Sc** scandium 21	48 **Ti** titanium 22	51 **V** vanadium 23	52 **Cr** chromium 24	55 **Mn** manganese 25	56 **Fe** iron 26	59 **Co** cobalt 27	59 **Ni** nickel 28	63.5 **Cu** copper 29	65 **Zn** zinc 30	70 **Ga** gallium 31	73 **Ge** germanium 32	75 **As** arsenic 33	79 **Se** selenium 34	80 **Br** bromine 35	84 **Kr** krypton 36
85 **Rb** rubidium 37	88 **Sr** strontium 38	89 **Y** yttrium 39	91 **Zr** zirconium 40	93 **Nb** niobium 41	96 **Mo** molybdenum 42	[98] **Tc** technetium 43	101 **Ru** ruthenium 44	103 **Rh** rhodium 45	106 **Pd** palladium 46	108 **Ag** silver 47	112 **Cd** cadmium 48	115 **In** indium 49	119 **Sn** tin 50	122 **Sb** antimony 51	128 **Te** tellurium 52	127 **I** iodine 53	131 **Xe** xenon 54
133 **Cs** caesium 55	137 **Ba** barium 56	139 **La*** lanthanum 57	178 **Hf** hafnium 72	181 **Ta** tantalum 73	184 **W** tungsten 74	186 **Re** rhenium 75	190 **Os** osmium 76	192 **Ir** iridium 77	195 **Pt** platinum 78	197 **Au** gold 79	201 **Hg** mercury 80	204 **Tl** thallium 81	207 **Pb** lead 82	209 **Bi** bismuth 83	[209] **Po** polonium 84	[210] **At** astatine 85	[222] **Rn** radon 86
[223] **Fr** francium 87	[226] **Ra** radium 88	[227] **Ac*** actinium 89	[261] **Rf** rutherfordium 104	[262] **Db** dubnium 105	[266] **Sg** seaborgium 106	[264] **Bh** bohrium 107	[277] **Hs** hassium 108	[268] **Mt** meitnerium 109	[271] **Ds** darmstadtium 110	[272] **Rg** roentgenium 111							

Elements with atomic numbers 112–116 have been reported but not fully authenticated

*The lanthanoids (atomic numbers 58–71) and the actinoids (atomic numbers 90–103) have been omitted.

The relative atomic masses of copper and chlorine have not been rounded to the nearest whole number.